ANCIENT ART FROM AFGHANISTAN

Catalogue of the Exhibition presented under the Patronage of
His Majesty King Mohammed Zaher Shah

Asia House Gallery, New York City
January 13–March 6, 1966

The Los Angeles County Museum of Art,
Lytton Gallery
March 25–May 16, 1966

National Collection of Fine Arts,
Smithsonian Institution, Washington, D.C.
June 29–August 23, 1966

ANCIENT ART FROM AFGHANISTAN

TREASURES OF THE KABUL MUSEUM

by Benjamin Rowland, Jr.

THE ASIA SOCIETY, INC. · *Distributed by Harry N. Abrams, Inc.*

ANCIENT ART FROM AFGHANISTAN is the catalogue of
an exhibition selected by Benjamin Rowland, Jr., Gleason Professor
of Fine Arts, Harvard University, and shown in the Asia House
Gallery in the winter of 1966 as an activity of The Asia Society, to
further greater understanding and mutual appreciation between the
United States and the peoples of Asia.

An Asia House Gallery Publication

Copyright 1966 by The Asia Society, Inc.

Printed in the United States of America

Library of Congress Catalogue Card Number: 66-11137

CONTENTS

BEGRĀM: 31. Woman standing under a *torāna*. Ivory; 16⅛ by 9½ inches (41 × 24 cm.).

It is with much personal satisfaction that I welcome you to this exhibition of the arts and artifacts of Afghanistan, depicting the rich and diverse cultural heritage of this ancient nation. This represents the first opportunity for the citizens of New York City and Los Angeles to see first-hand this comprehensive and representative collection.

I am reminded on this occasion that during my visit to America in 1963, I was indeed pleased to see an exhibition of Asian art on display at the galleries of The Asia Society in New York City. That exhibit revealed an expanding interest in Asia on the part of American viewers.

It is my sincere hope that this present important cultural event will further strengthen the friendly relations existing between the peoples of the United States and Afghanistan.

I would like to extend my cordial congratulations to those Americans and Afghans who worked so diligently in arranging this most worthy event.

MOHAMMED ZAHER SHAH
KING OF AFGHANISTAN

FOREWORD

Impressed with our own ease of movement and communication we tend to presume that the conquests of the farther reaches of international trade only began with us. We are, therefore, astonished when we learn that neither dangerous deserts nor sky-reaching mountains prevented a large traffic in goods across the whole vast continent of Asia before the time of Christ. This is one of the lessons of Asian archaeology, here taught with notable effectiveness through a display of excavated objects from the soil of Afghanistan. As Dr. Benjamin Rowland indicates in his learned and fascinating introduction to this catalogue, some of these "fragmented beauties" show that the Orient had a lively trade with various Mediterranean centers including Alexandrian Egypt—a point already foreseen by the reverse revelations of an Indian ivory of the first century A.D. discovered in the ruins of Pompeii, and Chinese porcelains found in an Egyptian tomb. So, it appears that the roads that crossed Afghanistan were not only the arteries of armies but also those of the determined merchants whose shuttlings wove together the remote lands of the ancient world.

The initiative in bringing these treasures of a famous Central Asian museum to New York was taken in 1963 by Mr. John D. Rockefeller 3rd, then President of the Asia Society, on the occasion of the reception at Asia House for King Mohammed Zaher Shah and Queen Homaira of Afghanistan. Mr. Rockefeller then expressed his hope that some of the unique possessions of the Kabul Museum might be lent to America and His Majesty replied by graciously promising to urge his government to allow this. Some time later, the Government of Afghanistan voted its agreement to the loan, also permitting the Asia House Gallery to offer the display to one other American institution. Happily, the Los Angeles County Museum of Art joins with us in presenting the exhibition, thus giving Americans on the West Coast as well as those on the East a chance to see these unusual works of art.

We wish to offer our depeest thanks to the royal patron of this exhibition, His Majesty King Mohammed Zaher Shah of Afghanistan, whose friendliness to our country has made the event possible. We also warmly thank the honorable members of the Government of Afghanistan who have confirmed the loan to the Asia Society. Two of the officials of this Government have been particularly helpful in making all the necessary arrangements, Mr. Mohammed Karim Barakzai, and Mr. Ahmad Ali Motamedi, Director General of the Kabul Museum, as have also Ambassador Dr. Abdul Majid and Mr. Mohammed Younos Rafik at the Embassy of Afghanistan in Washington, D.C. We are likewise deeply grateful to our own distinguished Ambassador in Kabul, the Honorable John M. Steeves, as well as to Mr. William D. Brewer, Chargé d'Affaires, and to Mr. Peter Edmonds and Mrs. Nancy Wolfe of our Embassy.

The debt of the Asia House Gallery to Dr. Benjamin Rowland is, of course, so large as to make any expression of appreciation inadequate. He visited Kabul on our behalf, thanks to a grant generously provided by the Asia Foundation, and carefully chose every work that is here shown. He also wrote this valuable catalogue and has greatly assisted Miss Virginia Field, editor, in obtaining the photographs for its illustrations. Some of these have been made available through the kindness of Dr. Vittorio Viale, Director of the Civic Museum of Turin; others by Nihon Keizai Shimbun, The Economic Journal of Japan, Tokyo; and still others from Dr. Rowland's and Dr. John Rosenfield's own personal files of negatives.

Besides our sense of gratitude to the Asia Foundation, we wish to acknowledge our deep obligation to The J.D.R. 3rd Fund of New York, whose Director is Mr. Porter McCray, for having provided the Asia House Gallery with the means of bringing these ancient arts, together with their curators, from Afghanistan to America.

GORDON BAILEY WASHBURN
Director, Asia House Gallery

ACKNOWLEDGMENTS

I must express my gratitude first of all to The Asia Society of New York and to The Asia Foundation for making possible the visit to Afghanistan in the spring of 1964, which enabled me to select the objects for this exhibition and to conduct the research necessary for the preparation of the catalogue. Special words of thanks are due to many friends in Kabul who facilitated my work in Afghanistan. I am indebted to Mr. Gaston Segur of the Asia Foundation and to Mr. William D. Brewer, Chargé d'Affaires at the American Embassy, for their many kindnesses and for arranging useful meetings with the Ministry of Education. The success of my trip was also assured by the friendly cooperation of Peter Edmonds and Nancy Wolfe of the American Embassy. I have the fondest memories of their hospitality, their efforts in facilitating my work in the museum at Darul Aman, and of our excursions to sites of archaeological interest in the Kabul region. I must also express my warm thanks to Mr. Ahmad Ali Motamedi and Mr. Mohammed Karim Barakzai of the Kabul Museum for their many courtesies in assisting my study and photographing of the treasures in the galleries and the storerooms of their wonderful museum. The preparation of this catalogue would have been impossible without the advice and editorial supervision of my wife. I must also express a debt of gratitude to my friend and colleague, John Max Rosenfield, for his patient and invaluable assistance in helping me to prepare the manuscript for publication and for his unfailingly generous suggestions on points of scholarship. Finally, I wish to thank Gordon Washburn and his staff for their continued support of this enterprise and for their editing of this work.

BENJAMIN ROWLAND, JR.
Gleason Professor of Fine Arts
Harvard University

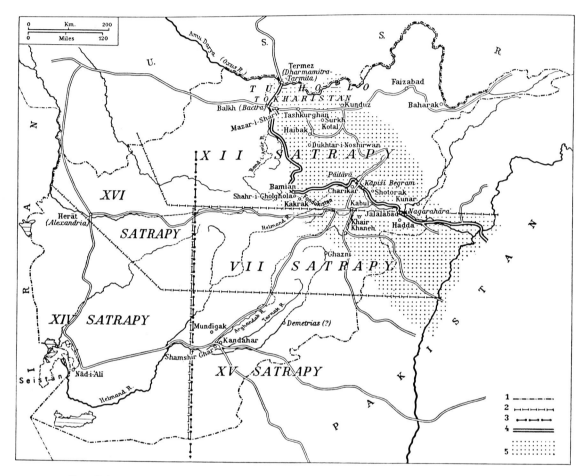

Map of Afghanistan

Afghanistan, showing principal centers and areas of art-historical importance: (1) Modern boundary; (2) Probable extent of the Achaemenid satrapies; (3) Probable limits of the Seleucid and Maurya dominions; (4) Bactria-Taxila caravan route; (5) Area of greatest concentration of finds of Gandhāran and post-Gandhāran art.

INTRODUCTION

In both the political and artistic sense Afghanistan, from ancient to modern times, may be designated as the crossroads of the world. This is a concept which Toynbee has defined as a roundabout, a civilization that absorbs influences from every quarter and then radiates them again to all points of the compass. In many periods of her early history Afghanistan was the hub of a wheel and its spokes were the trade routes, converging from and diverging to every region of the Mediterranean and Oriental worlds. This landlocked realm in the Asiatic heartland was also a watershed for the human driftwood left behind by the waves of invaders who, from earliest times, have broken over this fateful terrain.

Afghanistan, whose people are called *Beni-i Israel* or "Children of Israel" by Afghan chroniclers, and claimed as descendants of King Saul, was on the route of the Aryans who swept onward into India in the second millenium B.C.; here Alexander readied his phalanxes for his final assault on the Indian strongholds beyond the Khyber Pass. Some two centuries later, after the downfall of the Macedonian's successors in Bactria, the Indo-Scythian dynasty of the Kushans appeared as rulers of a vast empire extending from the Oxus to the Jumna River. The Persians conquered Afghanistan under Shāpur I in A.D. 241 and, after the fall of the Sasanian dynasty with the disaster of Nehawand in 632, it was not long before Islamic invaders from the West appeared in the Afghan valleys to still forever the heart of the Buddhist civilization created by the Kushans. The founders of later dynasties like the Ghaznavids were foreigners too, and Afghanistan was the homeland of the Mogul rulers of India. All of these now vanished conquerors, lost in the shadows of history long past, have left their imprint on the racial and artistic character of Afghan civilization. Parts of the modern population of Afghanistan are of Iranian origin. The ancestors of the Uzbeks and Hazaras were Turks and Mongols; the Kafirs, romantically identified as descendants of Alexander the Great, may be a racial remnant of the Aryan invasion; the Pathans, another ancient racial group, may be descended from the Aryans as well. Although Persian continues as the official language of the court and the language of literature, Afghanistan remains linguistically divided between Persian-speaking (Parsivan) groups and Pakhtu.

It is no wonder, in view of her turbulent history, that until modern times Afghanistan remained a region without racial or national unity. Afghanistan, the country governed by the Afghans, is a relatively modern term, and although to foreigners all the inhabitants of Afghanistan are known as Afghans, this term may be applied correctly only to the Durani clan, from which the ruling class has been drawn since the election of the soldier, Ahmad Khan, as Emir in 1747. From that moment this secluded Central Asian domain, which for so long has been a loose hegemony of tribes and almost continuously dominated by foreign conquerors, became a nation in the modern sense of the word.

The very geographical position of Afghanistan has contributed to the character of its civilization in every period of history. On the west Afghanistan is separated from Iran by the Harirud River and the deserts of Seistan. At various moments in history, as under Darius the Achaemenian and later under the Sasanians, large parts of Afghanistan were under Iranian rule and throughout its history Afghanistan has been dominated by Iranian taste in literature and the arts. On the north the Oxus River separates Afghanistan from Russian Turkestan. From this region came the Scythian and Turkish invaders in the early centuries of our era. To the east a thin strip of territory reaches out to Chinese Turkestan and the Pamir Range. This northeastern frontier is girdled by nearly impassable mountain barriers reinforced by the great curtain wall of the Hindu Kush. For millennia Afghanistan's southern neighbor has been India, more recently Pakistan, and throughout the centuries southern Afghanistan has been identified with cultural and political changes in the Indian sub-continent. Actually, the natural northern geographical boundary of India may be said to extend to the Shibar Pass, which divides the watershed of the Oxus from the basin of the Indus. To the north of this formidable cleft in the great mountain chain lies western Central Asia and the region of Afghanistan most closely linked with Iran.

The landscape of Afghanistan, in its many stupendous moods, presents an undreamed of vision of awesome splendor. This mountainous tract of ground, locked in the heart of the Asiatic continent, presents the most wild and impressive scenery in the world, and would have delighted the eighteenth century connoisseurs of the Sublime and the Picturesque as revelations of nature in her most irregular and titanic moods. The modern voyager in Afghanistan will always retain in memory the haunting beauty of this geographical fastness. Unforgettable in their silent desolation are the deserts west of Kandahar, scarred by sharp, serrated ridges like landscapes on the moon. One remembers, too, the savage beauty of the Jagdalik Pass, scene of the British disaster in the First Afghan War, or the wild defiles of the Bāmiyān River confined by precipices rising to eclipse the sun, or the breathtaking sublimity of the Bāmiyān Valley with the peaks of the Hindu Kush towering up like the throne of heaven itself. Afghanistan presents many prospects that are the Asiatic equivalent of the "Landscape with Ruins," the delight of the connoisseur of the Picturesque. Such are the skeletons of cities like Shahr-i-Gholghola, the turret-like *stupa* carved from solid rock at Haibak, or, silhouetted against the dusty sky, the *Minar* on the Chakri Hills over Kabul. Nature is transformed into architecture in the honeycomb of grottoes at Bāmiyān, and architecture aspires to the titanic shapes of mountains in the ruined *stupas* of the Jelalabad Plain. These shattered citadels, overgrown convents, and stumps of Buddhist pillars or Islamic minarets appear, as in any proper "Landscape with Ruins," as a part of the terrain, and, for the connoisseur of the Sublime, meditating on the theme of *Sic transit gloria mundi*, as symbols of what Volnay once described as "la révolution des empires." This spectacular amphitheater, the work of nature and man, has ringed the destinies of the Afghan people for millennia, and out of this earth, so often scorched and razed by savage conquerors, have appeared some of the greatest treasures of antiquity, Graeco-Roman, Buddhist, Hindu, and Islamic.

No traveler in Afghanistan can ever forget the myriad stars hanging suspended in the silent Central Asian night, and drifting like falling rockets to the horizon's rim, a spectacle that one instinctively recognizes as a vast archetypal dome that cups the world. No wonder that in every age of architecture men chose the dome to represent the vault of heaven itself—in the hemispheres of the Buddhist *stupas*, which were cosmic diagrams, in the Pantheon and Hagia Sophia, and in the domes of Islam. The ancient stellar deities of Babylon, of Iran, and Greece look down from this sky over Afghanistan, together with the constellations of the Islamic scientists. In the clarity of the night this celestial cupola, glowing with its always mysterious lights, seems especially designed by the demiurge to cover this land in the heart of Asia, a land with an immemorial history of human civilization in East and West.

The fragmented beauties of thousands of years of Afghan history are represented in the collections of the Kabul Museum, an institution unique in the world in being composed entirely of objects acquired, not by purchase, but by excavations in the native soil. The rooms of this building, originally built as a town hall by King Amanullah, have been filled largely by the extraordinary finds made by the French Archaeological Mission in Afghanistan, beginning in 1923 with the sensational discoveries at Hadda and culminating with the excavation of the national shrine of the Kushans at Surkh Kotal. The greatest single discovery of the French Mission, the treasure of Begrām, comprising an amazing collection of Graeco-Roman sculpture and artifacts, Indian ivories, and Chinese lacquers, is displayed in one of the most beautiful installations to be seen in any museum in the world. More recently the collections have been enriched by the work of the Italian Mission at Ghazni. The continued assistance of UNESCO experts has transformed other galleries dedicated to the antiquities of Bāmiyān and Fondukistan, and the vast stucco revetment of the mosque of Mahmud of Ghazni. Recent installations include a wing devoted to the sculpture and crafts of the Kafirs and the superb exhibition of Islamic objects from Ghazni. Other chapters in the history of Afghan civilization await representation in this collection. It is possible that even before these lines are printed the vanished treasures of Hellenistic Bactria, the Sasanian cities of Seistan, or new revelations of the Ghaznavid and Timurid cultures will have found their places in a museum which, in the repertory of the objects that it houses, shows the role Afghanistan has played at the *carrefour* of the world.

MUNDIGAK

The excavations conducted by a French Mission under the direction of Jean-Marie Casal at Mundigak, in the now desiccated region north of Kandahar in southwestern Afghanistan, have brought to light the remains of a civilization linking Afghanistan, Iran, and India of the Indo-Sumerian Period over a period extending from the late fourth to the late third millennium before Christ. The growth of this culture paralleled a similar development in Mesopotamia in the gradual urbanization of thriving village settlements. The earliest layers at Mundigak are contemporary with the Jamdet-Nasr Period of about 3000 B.C., and yielded pottery related to finds of approximate date at Susa and Anau and the earliest ceramic remains unearthed at Quetta in Baluchistan. Perhaps early in the third millennium there was an immigration of peoples from the region of Susiana, tribes who may have had an earlier ethnic relationship with the population of Mundigak.

The objects from Mundigak displayed in the exhibition were all recovered from the Fourth Level of the city's development, corresponding to ca. 2500 B.C. Pottery goblets in the shape of "brandy balloons" (Nos. 1 and 2), painted in black with representations of long-horned ibexes, are related to similar forms and patterns found at Susa and dating from about 2800 B.C. Similar designs occur on the pottery found at Kullu, Baluchistan, and other goblets with pipal leaf designs appear to link this material to familiar ceramic designs from Harappa. A further possible connection with Mohenjo Daro may be seen in terracotta figurines of the Mother Goddess and even more notably in the small stone head of a man (No. 3) which, in the mask-like simplicity of the face, has obvious connections with the Sumerian type of sculpture found at Mohenjo Daro. Apparently Mundigak was deserted—perhaps as the result of hostile invasion about 1500 B.C., and until its recent excavation was the domain of wanderers and shepherds who found shelter in the ruins of the citadel.

3

The objects from this site included in the present exhibition were excavated in the Fourth Level, the high point of this culture, and may be dated ca. 2500 B.C.

1

2

5

1. STEM CUP
    Painted clay; h. 5⅞ in. (15 cm.)
    KM 60.17.1420

The "brandy balloon" goblets or stem cups from Mundigak have counterparts in vessels found at sites of roughly the same period in the Indus Valley. The antelope design on the present example resembles similar long-horned beasts on the pottery of Susa II (ca. 2800 B.C.).

J. 1; I. 2; AAA 12; MDFA, XVII, Pl. XXXIIB.

2. STEM CUP
    Painted clay; h. 5¾ in. (14 cm.)
    KM 60.17.1413

Goblets of this type with representations of pipal leaves have also been found at Harappá and Chanhu Daro.

J. 2; I. 1; AAA 11; MDAFA, XVII, Pl. XXXIIA.

3. MALE HEAD
    Stone; h. 3½ in. (9 cm.)
    KM 63.1

This head with its mask-like formality, and in such details as the eyebrows in raised relief, strongly suggests the intrusion of Mesopotamian elements, as is also revealed by some of the famous statuettes found at Mohenjo Daro. (Cf. B. Rowland, *Art and Architecture of India*, Pl. I.)

J. 8, 4; AAA 17; MDAFA, XVII, Pls. XLIII, XLIV.

4. SEATED MALE FIGURE
    Baked clay; h. 3½ in. (9 cm.)
    KM 60.17.240

Probably a toy rather than a cult image, this object resembles others of the type unearthed at Chanhu Daro in the Indus Valley.

J. 7; I. 3; AAA 18

5. BULL'S HEAD
    Baked clay; h. 1⅞ in. (4.9 cm.)
    KM 60.17.181

This fragment corresponds to literally scores of similar representations of bovine creatures found in Baluchistan and along the Indus that are sometimes interpreted as evidence of a proto-historic cult of Śiva or local counterparts of the ancient bull deities of the Near East.

J. 9; AAA 19.

[For key to abbreviations see page 141.]

BEGRĀM: 28. Human-headed bird vase. Green glazed pottery; h. 4¾ inches (12 cm.).

Fig. 1. The Hindu Kush and the Panjir River from the Ramparts of Begrām.

BEGRAM

Famous in the annals of the Chinese pilgrims was the ancient city of Kāpiśa, which Hsüan-tsang noted was the summer capital of the great Kushans and the asylum of the Chinese hostages whom Kanishka held from the kingdom of Kashgar. Some modern scholars have suggested that the Kushan city was raised on the foundations of Alexandria-under-Caucasus, a city founded by the Macedonian conqueror, and it is conceded by most that it may correspond to the site of Nissa, another town mentioned in the chronicle of Alexander's conquest. The location of this famous ancient city has been fixed at Begrām, some forty miles north of Kabul near Charikar. Although Begrām-Kāpiśa, like most of the famous archaeological sites in Afghanistan, was superficially explored in the nineteenth century, it remained for the French Archaeological Mission to begin serious excavations in 1937. The digging, which continued until the first year of the

World War, brought to light one of the greatest treasures in the history of Asiatic archaeology.

The ramparts of ancient Begrām overlook the Panjir River and the mighty bastion of the Hindu Kush. (Fig. 1). The modern hamlet which lies below the citadel, like fortified manors all over Afghanistan, is built of mud bricks and resembles, one suspects, the architecture of the Kāpiśa of old. Near the village a decrepit ferry on a cable crosses the torrent of the Panjir. Beyond are marshes, which in the spring are the feeding grounds for flocks of white storks and ducks. In the further distance, beyond the stands of mulberry and chanar trees, open the passes which today, as in classical times, lead northward to Bactria and Central Asia.

The ruins of Begrām represent three moments in the life and death of this famous city. The original foundations were laid out on a plan not markedly different from Hellenistic cities such as Dura Europos. This was the capital of the last of the Indo-Greek kings and the first rulers of the Kushan dynasty. The second Begrām, modified only by the construction of new palaces and fortifications, was the northern capital of Kanishka and his successors. There is evidence that this town was violently destroyed by fire, probably at the time of the disastrous invasion of the Sasanians under Shāpur I in 241. A final settlement arose on the ruins of these earlier capitals and was probably abandoned for the last time with the coming of the Hephthalites in the fifth century.

The great discoveries were made in 1937 and the following years in a number of chambers in Kanishka's palace complex that apparently had been walled up, presumably at the approach of a dangerous invader. These storerooms were littered with a vast accumulation of objects from literally every corner of the world. The finds comprised fragments of Chinese lacquer boxes, Graeco-Roman statuettes in bronze, a collection of Roman glassware of every conceivable variety, Graeco-Roman vessels of porphyry and alabaster, and an extraordinary group of plaster casts apparently taken from classical metalwork. In addition to all this, the treasure rooms yielded a large number of superb Indian ivory carvings that had originally served as the revetments of various articles of furniture. Many of these objects present us with types and techniques that are otherwise unknown in collections of classical and Indian art.

Turning our attention first to the Graeco-Roman bronze statuettes, we find that two of the objects, namely, the statuettes of Hercules-Serapis (No. 7) and Harpocrates, the god of silence (No. 10), point to the Alexandrian origin of the classical material. This connection with Roman Egypt is suggested again by the porphyry bowl (No. 30) carved from a stone which in Roman times was quarried only in lower Egypt. The Alexandrian origin of the classical components of the Begrām treasure is further suggested by certain types of glassware, notably a beaker (an object too fragile to be included in the present exhibition) carved with a representation of that wonder of the world, the Pharos, the

famous lighthouse of Alexandria, as well as by some of the examples of painted glass in the collection. Although examples of this type of glassware painted with mythological and genre subjects have been found all over western Europe, the beautiful goblet in the Begrām collection with a representation of Isis again points to the Alexandrian origin of this ware (No. 21). The Begrām collection also contains a number of specimens of a peculiarly baroque glassware, in which the vase itself has a surround of glass ribbons encasing the amphora—like the raffia covering of a Chianti bottle (No. 27). To these types would have to be added the vases with a pressed honeycomb design, the perfume flasks in the shape of dolphins, and a particularly beautiful plate executed in the millefiori technique.

Among the most surprising of the classical objects in the treasure room at Begrām were some fifty plaster casts of Greek metalwork (Nos. 12–20). The plaster medallions at Begrām are presumably replicas of the *emblema* or centerpieces of silver salvers of Hellenistic and Roman date. The repertory includes subjects from the mythological cycle of

Fig. 2. Roman gem with representation of Ganymede and the Eagle of Zeus.

Fig. 3. Ivory mirror handle, Indian, first century A.D. From Pompeii. Collection of Museo Nazionale, Naples.

Dionysus and Aphrodite, genre scenes, profile portraits, and the ideal busts in high relief. Although nearly identical representations of many of the subjects of the Begrām plaster plaques can be found in Graeco-Roman art (Fig. 2), it appears highly likely that these casts were all made from specimens of Greek metalwork extant in the Imperial period.

It was of course comparatively easy to make copies of such metal reliefs by first preparing a plaster cast and then producing a mold in metal or clay, from which other replicas could be cast in plaster or silver. A large collection of similar facsimiles of Greek silverware, together with terracotta molds, was found at Memphis early in the present century, and other examples have come to light at Sabratha in North Africa. Masterworks of Greek silverwork were prized by Roman collectors, and Pliny mentions the payment of 10,000 *denarii* for a bowl by Pythras, representing the struggle of Odysseus and Diomedes for the palladium. With the unprecedented demand for the masterworks of Greek silverware it became necessary to provide replicas of these already scarce items. It has been supposed that the purpose of such a collection of plaster facsimiles as those found at Begrām was to provide models for metalworkers and samples for prospective clients.

The Begrām casts appear to have been taken from originals of a number of different periods, the earliest going back to the fourth century B.C. and the latest from Roman metalware of the Augustan to the Antonine period. It is tempting to think that the Odysseus of No. 17, which has a companion plaque with the portrayal of Diomedes, is a facsimile of the famous vessel referred to by Pliny. Other reliefs, like the slaughter of a pig (No. 19), recall the pictorial reliefs of Hellenistic times, and the veiled lady of No. 13 has been identified as a portrait of the Empress Livia. One subject at least, the erotic scene of No. 15, is found in an identical relief of the late Hellenistic period. It should be noted that one actual example of a silver *emblema*, a disk with the representation of the Oriental Dionysus, was found at Taxila in a treasure secreted before the Kushan invasion in the middle of the first century A.D.

It may be supposed that this collection of plaster medallions was, like the glassware and metal sculpture, of Alexandrian origin. Many of the plaques were pierced so that they could be suspended as decorations or for display. As suggested above, they may have been imported as samples for clients to order replicas in silver to be made by local artisans or, it is perhaps not too much to conjecture, to place orders for metal copies to be made in Alexandria.

No less important than the magnificent collection of classical objects are the great numbers of Indian ivory plaques and figurines (Nos. 31–46). It is apparent at once in examining these beautiful specimens of carving in miniature that not only do they illustrate a variety of techniques, but also that they date from a number of different periods. Some of the plaques are carved in very high relief, often with reticulated backgrounds; others are executed in a sort of sunken relief with a heavy emphasis on the contours; still other panels, both in ivory and bone, are really incised drawings or engravings, rather than carvings. Examples of sculpture in the round were also found, notably a group of river goddesses. A few small examples of this technique are included in the present collection.

One of the favorite compositions of the Begrām panels represents two women, *yakshīs* or courtesans, standing under a *torāna* or gateway like the famous portals of Sānchī (Nos. 31–33). Their stocky proportions and opulent forms, composed in an additive rather than organic fashion, remind us of the famous figures of *yakshīs* from this same Indian site. In this connection one should mention the superb carved ivory mirror handle, with the representation of a courtesan and her handmaids, which was found in the Via dell' Abbondanza at Pompeii (Fig. 3). The style of this beautiful object, which

must of course be dated prior to A.D. 79, is, like that of the earliest of the Begrām plaques, a miniature version of the Early Āndhra style.

The enticing figures of women on other sets of plaques from Begrām are just as unmistakably related to the *yakshīs* of the Mathurā school. The date of the florescence of this Indian style under the Kushans is not clearly fixed, but is believed to have coincided with the reign of the great Kanishka and his immediate successors in the second and early third centuries. In these plaques the ladies parade their charms in an even more provocative fashion. Like their counterparts in stone, the famous courtesans of the railing pillars of Mathurā, the proportions have become more elongated, the poses more pliant and consciously graceful, and, in contrast to the forms of the earliest ivory carvings, the bodies are articulated in a more truly organic manner.

The magnificent console with the representation of a rider on a leogryph emerging from a *makara* mouth (No. 40) is, of course, reminiscent of similar motifs in the sculpture of Mathurā and Amarāvatī, but the exquisite refinement in the execution of this composition and its details surpasses any example known in the stone sculpture of Kushan Mathurā. One wonders if, even as late as the second century A.D., the really great masters worked in ivory—and the stone carvers were still striving to approximate the refinement of their technique. The Begrām collection also includes a great many panels which are really engraved drawings on ivory or bone, which, in the uniqueness of their subject matter and technique, defy comparison with monumental examples of stone carving. The voluptuous seated woman of No. 35 suggests the taste of the sculptors of the Mathurā *yakshīs*, but the strange combination of hunters and beasts entwined in a mesh of ribbon-like interlaced patterns (Nos. 45, 46)—almost suggestive of Scythian ornament—has no parallels in Indian sculpture and is more likely a reflection of a lost school of Indian painting.

Summing up the evidence for the date of the

Begrām treasure, the majority of the classical objects are datable in the first century of our era or earlier, with only a few objects suggesting a dating as late as the Antonine period. The fragments of Chinese lacquer are no later than the second century, and the collection of Indian ivories includes pieces that are counterparts of the Early Āndhra school of sculpture and others related to the Mathurā style of the second century A.D.

It has been suggested that the treasure rooms at Begrām were sealed off in the year 241, when King Shāpur of Iran led an invasion that ended the Great Kushan dynasty. One objection to this date is that it is so late in relation to the age of the objects. All of them would already have been antiques, as much as one hundred to two hundred years old. If these works were part of a royal collection their antiquity at the time of the closing of the storerooms would be of no particular moment; but if, as has been also suggested, they were a merchant's stock in trade which for some reason was impounded, it is hard to believe an importer would have offered a stock of objects already several hundred years old.

There is no existing historical document which explains why this valuable treasure was buried and never reclaimed, but there is no lack of evidence that the Kushan dynasty was afflicted with the same kind of political instability that beset the later rulers of the region. Uprisings against the dynasty, struggles among pretenders to the throne, separatist movements—any of these could have led to the burning of a palace, a siege of the city, and the hurried sealing off of the treasure for protection.

Numismatists have noted a strange change in Kushan coinage after the death of the great Emperor Kanishka. The coins of his successor, Huvishka, at first retain the fine standards of Kanishka, but these are succeeded by barbarized coins which, though bearing Huvishka's name, are full of blundered legends and crude images. This series is presently replaced by a return to a highly disciplined, fine quality of coinage still under the name of Huvishka—numismatic testimony, perhaps, for a return to political stability.

Similarly, the dynastic shrines of the Kushans excavated at Surkh Kotal in Afghanistan and at Mathurā in northern India both offer epigraphic suggestions that, having been abandoned or dilapidated, they were restored in the time of Huvishka, a further indication of political turmoil. These events occurred roughly within the first half of the second century A.D., close to the dates of the latest components of the Begrām hoard.

The Begrām treasure, especially the number and variety of Graeco-Roman imports, provides the strongest possible proof of close commercial and cultural relations between the Kushans and the Roman world. It far surpasses, in the number and variety of the objects found, the discoveries of works of classical origin at Taxila, Kohlapur, and Arikamedhu. Whether the presence of such a treasure trove of classical luxury goods in the palace compound at Kāpiśa could have exercised any influence on the art of the region is open to question. But the very presence of this material would certainly seem to indicate a prevalent taste for Graeco-Roman art that makes the florescence of the Indo-Roman school of Gandhāra easier to understand.

At the same time the superb collection of ivories from Begrām introduces us to a hitherto almost unknown aspect of early Indian art, one that seems to have the closest possible connection with the stylistic and technical development of monumental sculpture in early India.

9

The treasure of Begrām, site of a Kushan palace, consists of small works of art in many media from China, the Roman world, and India. The classical artifacts in bronze, porphyry, glass, and plaster may be dated no later than the second century A.D. by their correspondence with similar types in Roman Egypt and other parts of the Mediterranean world. The style of some of the Indian ivories closely resembles the stone carving of the Early Classic period in India (ca. second century B.C. to first century A.D.). Others are related to the sculpture of Mathurā of the second century A.D. The fragments of Chinese lacquer (not shown) have been dated in the second century of our era. Although it has been suggested that the whole collection was hidden at the approach of the Sasanian invaders in 241, it seems likely that it disappeared into the palace treasury at least one hundred years earlier, so that it would be possible to date the majority of the objects comprised in this remarkable hoard in the first or early second century A.D.

11

7

10

8

BRONZES

6. HORSEMAN
Bronze; h. 5⅜ in. (13.5 cm.)
KM 57.39

A similar bronze rider, perhaps representing Alexander the Great wearing an elephant headdress, is in the collection of the Metropolitan Museum of Art. It was reputedly found at Athribis in the Nile Delta, a circumstance which supports the Egyptian origin of the Kabul example. (Cf. M. Bieber, *The Sculpture of the Hellenistic Age*, fig. 298.) (Not illustrated.)

MDAFA, XI, fig. 335.

7. HERCULES-SERAPIS
Bronze; h. 9⅝ in. (24.5 cm.)
KM 57.34

This beautiful statuette with its svelte Lysippic canon is a syncretic fusion of Hercules and the Egyptian Serapis, elsewhere unknown in ancient art and literature. Hercules has his familiar attributes of the club and the golden apples of the Hesperides and wears the modius or crown of olive leaves emblematic of the fertility of the Nile. In this guise, the Greek god has perhaps assumed the role of Osiris as guardian of the world of the dead.

J. 15; I. 23; tav. X; MDAFA, XI, figs. 323, 325.

8. SHIELD WITH MOBILE FISHES
Bronze; diam. 15⅜ in. (39 cm.)
KM 57.77

This Graeco-Roman "mobile" has been identified as either a shield or a table ornament. The fins and tails of the fishes on the floor of the dish were moved by small lead weights attached by wires and hidden beneath the surface of the vessel.

I. 27, tav. XIII; MDAFA, IX, 48–52; MDAFA, XI, 356.

9. WEIGHT IN SHAPE OF BUST OF ATHENA
Bronze; h. 3½ in. (9 cm.)
KM 57.134

Many bronze weights in anthropomorphic shapes representing both gods and rulers are known in examples from Graeco-Roman to Byzantine times. They were attached by chains to the arm of the balance or steelyard, and their shape may have evolved from perfume bottles of a similar form.

J. 16; MDAFA, IX, figs. 58, 59; AAA 70.

10. HARPOCRATES
Bronze; h. 5¼ in. (13.3 cm.)
KM 57.36

A similar figure of Harpocrates, the Egyptian god of silence, was found at Taxila and is also of Alexandrian origin. (Cf. Sir John Marshall, *Taxila*, Cambridge, 1951, Pl. 196 E.) The soft modeling and the *déhanchement* in an S-curve suggest a derivation from an earlier Praxitelean type. (The photograph from which the illustration was made was taken before the statuette was properly restored with the finger held to the lips.)

MDAFA, XI, figs. 322 and 324.

11. VESSEL WITH TWO HANDLES
Bronze; h. 13⅜ in. (34 cm.)
KM 57.4

This shallow bowl, suggestive of the classic kylix shape, may be compared with other elegant domestic utensils found at Pompeii and Herculaneum.

J. 19; AAA 75.

12

15

17

13

19

18

14

16

PLASTER MEDALLIONS

12. BUST OF A YOUTH
Plaster; diam. 8¾ in. (22.3 cm.)
KM 57.144

A number of examples of metalwork from the treasures of Boscoreale and Hildesheim were ornamented with similar busts in high relief in the central section or *emblema*. This large plaque, measuring nearly a foot in diameter, has a representation of a youthful male figure, sometimes identified as a portrayal of Menander, and may have been cast from a wall decoration rather than a salver.

J. 26; I. 19, tav. VII; AAA 24; MDAFA, XI, 313–315.

13. PORTRAIT OF LIVIA
Plaster; diam. 5¼ in. (13.5 cm.)
KM 57.149

Represented in this medallion is a lady with a veil covering a diadem in the form of the aegis of Athena. This noblewoman was identified by E. A. Voretzsch as a portrait of the Empress Livia who was often shown in the guise of the Olympian goddesses. (E. A. Voretzsch, in *Römische Mitteilungen*, Deutsches Archäologisches Institut, 64, 1957, 6–45.)

J. 23; I. 11, tav. IV; AAA 30; MDAFA, XI, fig. 302.

14. ARES
Plaster; diam. 4⅞ in. (12.5 cm.)
KM 57.155

Duplicates from the same mold exist in the collections at Kabul and in the Musée Guimet. The youthful warrior has been recognized as a portrait of Alexander the Great as the god of war. The same figure is to be seen in gems and coins of the Graeco-Roman period. (Cf. MDAFA, XI, figs. 438, 442, 443.)

J. 28; I. 9, tav. III; AAA 33; MDAFA, XI, figs. 299, 437.

15. EROTIC SYMPLEGMA
Plaster; diam. 6½ in. (16.5 cm.)
KM 57.151

Although sometimes identified as a portrayal of Selene and Endymion, the subject, as suggested by Otto Kurz, may be a figuration of nightmare with a winged siren, or *lasa*, descending to ravish a sleeping traveler. A marble version of the subject, probably of late Hellenistic date, is in the reserve collection of the Museum of Fine Arts, Boston (MDAFA, XI, fig. 416, and C. Vermeule in *American Journal of Archaeology*, Oct. 1964, fig. 24).

J. 34; I. 18, tav. VIII; AAA 27; MDAFA, XI, figs. 291, 415.

16. GANYMEDE AND THE EAGLE OF ZEUS
Plaster; diam. 5 in. (12.8 cm.)
KM 57.156

Many versions of the subject of Ganymede and the Eagle of Zeus are to be found in terra-cotta plaques and engraved gems of the Graeco-Roman period. (Cf. Paolo Alessandro Maffei, *Gemme antiche figurate*, Rome, 1707, Pl. 29.)

MDAFA, XI, figs. 296, 417.

17. ODYSSEUS
Plaster; diam. 4⅜ in. (11 cm.)
KM 57.178

The famous sardonyx by the master Felix, formerly in the collection of Captain Spencer-Churchill, reproduces the subject of the struggle of Odysseus and Diomedes for the Palladium (Cf. Domenico Braccia, *Memorie degli antichi incisori . . . in gemme e cammei*, Florence, 1786, Pl. LXXV). The figure of Diomedes appears, in what must have been a companion piece to this plaque, in the Kabul collection. Together they may have been casts of the renowned piece of Greek metalwork, mentioned by Pliny as having been sold for the huge sum of 10,000 *denarii*.

J. 30; I. 13, tav. VI; MDAFA, XI, figs. 308, 445; AAA 28.

18. TYCHE OF ALEXANDRIA
    Plaster; diam. 6⅞ in. (17.5 cm.)
    KM 57.153

Similar reclining female figures, recognized as representations of the Tyche or Fortune of Alexandria, appear on the coins of Trajan and Antoninus Pius.

I. 12, tav. V; MDAFA, XI, figs. 303, 422.

19. SACRIFICE OF A PIG
    Plaster; diam. 6⅛ in. (15.5 cm.)
    KM 57.150

This subject, possibly of ritual significance but more likely a genre scene, has the typical pictorial treatment of the background seen in Hellenistic marble reliefs.

J. 32; I. 15, tav. V; AAA 35; MDAFA, XI, figs. 290, 397.

20. SLEEPING MAENAD
    Plaster; diam. 6⅞ in. (17.5 cm.)
    KM 57.154

It has been suggested that this plaque in high relief may be a cast of a metal ornament fixed to the curved back-rest of a couch or *kline*. Although the figure bears some resemblance to the famous Ariadne of the Vatican, the disheveled, "blowzy" type strongly supports an identification as a companion of Dionysus.

J. 25; I. 7, tav. I; AAA 23; MDAFA, XI, figs. 280, 395.

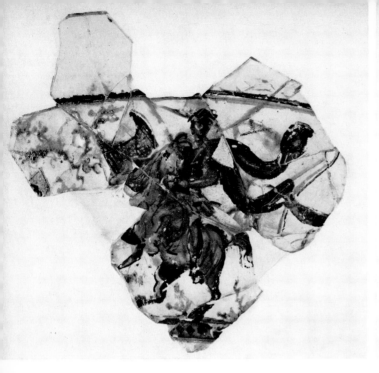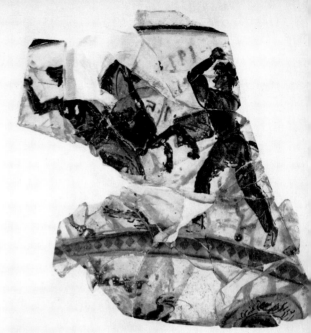

22

BEGRĀM: 21. Goblet. Painted glass; h. 5¼ inches (13.5 cm.).

27

24

30

50   29

GLASS

21. GOBLET
Painted glass; h. 5¼ in. (13.5 cm.)
KM 58.1.3

Like all the specimens of this ware found at Begrām, this beaker is painted in thick brilliant colors that impart an enamel-like relief to the surface of the glass. Although the central figure has been identified as Isis, the composition may simply be a genre subject representing figures plaiting garlands. Probably, together with the other glassware from Begrām, this object was imported from Alexandria by the maritime route which became popular with the discovery of the monsoon winds in the first century.

J. 38; I. 29, tav. XIV; AAA 2; MDAFA, XI, figs. 371, 372; MDAFA, IX, 29–32.

22. FRAGMENTS OF PAINTED GLASS
H. 3¾ in. (9.5 cm.)
KM 58.1.5A and 5B

Represented are cavalrymen and foot soldiers in combat, the counterparts of similar subjects frequently found in Roman mosaics.

J. 39, 41; AAA 87, 89; I. 31, tav. XVI; MDAFA, IX, 34.

23. FRAGMENT OF PAINTED GLASS
3⅛ x 4 in. (8 x 10 cm.)
KM 58.1.7

This fragment of a large bowl is painted in a sketchy, fluid manner, suggestive of the technique often seen in Roman wall-paintings. The subject has sometimes been identified as Persephone in Hades. (Not illustrated.)

J. 41; I. 32, tav. XVII; MDAFA, XI, fig. 267.

24. GOBLET
White glass; h. 5⅛ in. (13 cm.)
KM 57.2.64

Glasses with an impressed lozenge or honeycomb pattern have been found in Cyprus, at Pompeii, and in many parts of the Mediterranean world. They are generally dated in the first century A.D. The technique survives in Iranian glassware of the Sasanian period and later.

J. 44; I. 35, tav. XIV; AAA 78; MDAFA, XI, fig. 252.

25. ICHTHYOMORPHIC FLASK
White glass; h. 3¾ in. (9.4 cm.)
KM 57.222

Similar examples of ichthyomorphic vessels, probably used as perfume flasks, have been found in all parts of Europe. They may be dated in the first century A.D. and later, and all are believed to be of Alexandrian origin.

J. 50; AAA 81; MDAFA, IX, fig. 41.

26. MILLEFIORI DISH
Diam. 7 in. (17.7 cm.)
KM 57.190

Millefiori vessels were made by lining a mold of the desired shape with sections of multicolored glass rods packed side by side and then heated until these rods melted and fused to make a continuous and ever-variegated fabric. Particularly beautiful examples are to be seen in the collections of the British Museum.

J. 37; I. 42; AAA 1; MDAFA, IX, figs. 9, 10.

27. FRAGMENT OF AMPHORA
Blue glass; h. 6⅜ in. (16.3 cm.)
KM 57.277

This elegant vessel with handles formed of ribbons of glass represents still another intricate technique practised in Alexandria.

J. 49; AAA 82.

POTTERY

28. HUMAN-HEADED BIRD VASE
Green glazed pottery; h. 4¾ in. (12 cm.)
KM 57.290

An iridescent, greenish lead glaze, an example of a technique developed in Alexandria in the first century A.D., covers this flask in the shape of a human-headed bird. The fact that the head has a strangely Indian look may indicate that this was an exotic object made especially for export in the eastern trade.

J. 87; I. 43, tav. XIX; AAA 4; MDAFA, XI, 241, 242.

STONE

29. OENOCHOE
Alabaster; h. 6¾ in. (17 cm.)
KM 57.189

This is a replica in alabaster of a type of Greek vessel known in many examples in bronze, glass, and pottery.

J. 86; AAA 91; MDAFA, IX, 13, 14.

30. PORPHYRY DISH
Diam. 7¼ in. (18.4 cm.)
KM 57.185

A type of stone which was quarried and worked only at Mons Porphyrites in Egypt during the Roman period was used for this dish.

J. 85; AAA 92; MDAFA, XI, fig. 354 bis.

33

36

34

38

37

39

35

45

44

IVORIES

31. WOMEN STANDING UNDER A TORĀNA

Ivory; 16⅛ x 9½ in. (41 x 24 cm.)

KM 58.1.65

This plaque is one of a large number of panels originally forming parts of the decoration of a large throne. The carving of the rather full, squat figures of the women suggests the style of the stone reliefs of the gateways at Sāñchī of the first century A.D. The *torāna* or gateway with its three architraves also suggests the portals of this and other monuments of the early classic period in India.

J. 54; AAA 3; MDAFA, XI, 8.

32. WOMEN STANDING UNDER AN ARCHED GATE

Ivory; 13⅜ x 7¼ inches (34 x 18.5 cm.)

KM 58.1.81

The technique of this plaque combines incised linear engraving with high relief and openwork. As in many other examples from the same series, the pointed arch under which the women are placed is a representation of a typical portal from an Indian *chaitya* hall like Bhājā or Kārlī.

J. 55; AAA 41; MDAFA, XI, 94.

33. TWO WOMEN UNDER AN ARCHED GATE AND A WOMAN WITH A PARROT UNDER A TORĀNA

Ivory; 5¼ x 6⅞ in. (13.5 x 17.5 cm.)

KM 58.1.26

One of a number of such panels originally decorating a piece of wooden furniture; in this fragment, as in the preceding panels, the women wear the beaded aprons and heavy anklets that adorn the *yakshīs* of Sāñchī and the even earlier figures in the Buddhist railing of Bhārhut.

J. 56; AAA 41.

34. STANDING WOMAN

Ivory; h. 3⅝ in. (9.3 cm.)

KM 59.1.135

Isolated from its setting, this fragment reveals to particular advantage the full sensuous beauty of the early classic style of Indian sculpture.

J. 60; AAA 49.

35. SEATED WOMAN

Bone; 3 x 2⅜ in. (7.5 x 5.9 cm.)

KM 59.1.16

In this bone panel, the contour of the seated female figure is heavily engraved into the face of the plaque with a faint suggestion of very low relief modeling within the thick outline. The figure, still archaic in conception, recalls the warm, sensuous canon of Indian sculpture of the Early Classic Period.

J. 73; I. 54, tav. xxv; AAA 56.

36. LION

Ivory; h. 1¾ in. (4.5 cm.)

KM 59.1.57

This tiny fragment, representing the head and foreparts of a crouching lion, probably formed one of the feet of a small stool. The naturalistic representation of the leonine form is in marked contrast to the usually conventionalized portrayal of these beasts in Early Āndhra and Kushan sculpture, so that in this respect the object is more evocative of Hellenistic representations of lions.

J. 63; AAA 69.

37. TRITON

Ivory; 4⅛ x 3⅛ in. (10.5 x 8 cm.)

KM 59.1.181

The subject of this relief is frequently encountered in the stone carving of Mathurā of the second and third centuries A.D. The present example represents a later transformation of the Indian snake-legged tritons; here a pair of flanking *makaras* seem to be devouring the legs of the central figure and the formerly piscine bodies and tails of the Indian crocodiles have been changed into ornamental foliate shapes.

J. 64; AAA 47; MDAFA, IX, figs. 73, 74; MDAFA, XI, fig. 522.

38. JAR OF ABUNDANCE
Ivory; h. 4¾ in. (12 cm.)
KM 59.1.274

A vase of abundance filled with lotus flowers and supported by a crouching *yaksha* is a motif frequently found in the Kushan sculpture of Mathurā, as well as in the limestone carvings of the *stupa* of Amarāvatī.

J. 65; AAA 48; MDAFA, XI, fig. 533.

39. ELEPHANT AND WARRIOR
Ivory; 3⅛ x 5¼ in. (8 x 13.5 cm.)
KM 58.1.201

This subject is repeated either identically or in reverse in a number of other ivory panels from Begrām. The technique is characteristic of a considerable group of the Begrām *plaquettes*, in which the design could be described as an incised drawing, rather than carving. The subject may be pure genre without reference to any epic source but it suggests that chivalric royal imagery mentioned as appropriate for royal thrones in texts like the *Manasāra*.

J. 78; AAA 59; MDAFA, XI, fig. 101.

40. CONSOLE WITH RIDER ON A LEOGRYPH
Ivory; 10 x 6¾ in. (25.4 x 17 cm.)
KM 58.1.152

This beautiful fragment represents a female figure riding a leogryph emerging from the open mouth of a *makara*, while a small attendant, standing on the jaws of the monster, supports the rider's foot.

The object, carved on both sides, was evidently a console doweled to support the arm of a throne. The motif of the winged leogryph was a favorite one in the architectural brackets of Mathurā and Amarāvatī, but none of these Indian stone examples can match the sophistication of carving in the Begrām ivory. A later, decadent form of leogryph appears in the architectural decoration at Bāmiyān (No. 81).

J. 53; AAA 40; MDAFA, XI, figs. 152–155 and 518–520.

41. and 42. FRIEZE WITH SEATED WOMEN IN FLORAL SCROLL
Ivory; 2⅜ x 12⅜ in. (6 x 31.5 cm.)
KM 58.1.256 and KM 58.1.258

The subjects of nearly all of the Begrām ivories are profane, and invariably the settings are inhabited exclusively by women. The present examples are parts of a very long frieze, in which female couples, separated by the twining of an endless Aśoka branch, are engaged in conversation. The groups are separated by bird masks framed in spiraling leaf motifs. As in so many of the Begrām ivories, the background is cut away in order to set off the reticulated, carved pattern against the wooden surface to which it was attached. (Not illustrated.)

J. 83, 84; MDAFA, XI, figs. 170, 172.

43. TIGERS AND BIRDS
Ivory; 1⅞ x 8⅛ in. (4.3 x 20.5 cm.)
KM 58.1.219

J. 69; AAA 53; MDAFA, XI, fig. 202.

44. TWO BIRDS
Ivory; 3⅛ x 5⅛ in. (7.5 x 13 cm.)
KM 58.1.204

These engraved animals might be compared to the Kushan period portions of the Buddhist railing at Bodh Gayā. Their lively characterization seems to anticipate the animal caricatures of the famous Japanese drawings of Tōba Sōjō.

J. 70; I. 53, tav. XXVI; AAA 54; MDAFA, XI, fig. 200.

45. and 46. HUNTING SCENES
Ivory; 2⅞ x 9½ in. (7.3 x 24 cm.) and 2¾ x 9½ in. (7.1 x 24 cm)
KM 58.1.124, 125; KM 58.1.126, 127.

The technique used in these fragments—parts of a very long frieze that presumably decorated one of the elaborate thrones found in the treasure room—is pure incision with double contour lines for some of the elements in the composition. These contours are reinforced with red and black pigment, an indication of what was perhaps a general practice of the Begrām ivory-workers. The compositions are among the most picturesque and fantastic of all the Begrām ivory drawings. Represented are hunters with bows engaged in shooting winged felines framed in mazes of twining branches or in stylized rocky grottoes.

J. 76, 77; I. 44, 45, tav. XVIII; AAA 50, 51; MDAFA, XI, figs. 104–107.

Fig. 4. Cover and sides of an ivory jewel casket, second-third century A.D. Collection of the Kabul Museum. (Not in exhibition.)

GANDHARA SCULPTURE

AT PAITAVA AND SHOTORAK

The sites of Pāitāvā and Shotorak, within a few miles of Begrām, were excavated by members of the French Archaeological Mission before the Second World War. Shotorak is believed to have been the dwelling place of King Kanishka's Chinese hostages, and the plan of the monastery corresponds closely to those of the religious establishments at Taxila. The sculptured decoration of both of these *sangharamas* consisted for the most part of carving in the familiar blue-grey schist of Gandhāra. It is evident at once that both the images of Buddha and narrative reliefs belong to a late period of the Gandhāra school and were probably carved no earlier than the third century A.D. The relief of Dipankara Buddha (No. 47) shows us a figure in which all sense of the earlier classical proportion has been lost. The image has an hieratic rigidity suggestive of the Romano-Parthian sculpture of Hatra and Palmyra, and this resemblance extends to the treatment of the drapery. By means of a series of string-like, quilted ridges, the folds are reduced to a schematic, linear formula, producing an effect far from the realistic presentation of a voluminous classical garment such as we see in Gandhāra Buddha images of the first and second centuries. The same hieratic rigidity and frontality prevails in other reliefs, such as the panel of Maitreya from Pāitāvā that again reminds us of the half Roman, half Oriental style of Palmyra and Dura Europos. Only one carving from these sites, the monumental relief of Buddha and the Kāśyapas from Shotorak, still has some suggestion of the deeply carved, illusionistic technique of the Gandhāra style of the second century. These fragments of slate sculpture from the region of Begrām are of great importance as illustrations of the final phase of the Gandhāra style that was destined to exercise a far greater influence on Buddhist sculpture in Central Asia, and even in China, than the earlier, more classical examples of the style.

48

The Buddhist reliefs from these two monastic sites in the Begrām area are late provincial versions of the Indo-Roman sculpture of Gandhāra in northwest Pakistan and may be dated in the third century A.D. or even later.

47

49

51

50

47. DIPANKARA BUDDHA
Slate; h. 32⅞ in. (83.5 cm.)
KM 61.7.13 (from Shotorak)

The relief illustrates the legend of the last Buddha of the Past, who predicts the advent of the last Buddha Gautama. According to the Chinese pilgrim Hsüan-tsang, the scene of the Dipankara Jataka was Nagarahāra, near modern Jelalabad, and this may account for the popularity of the subject at Shotorak. The panel illustrates the first part of the miracle in which, at the left, the young Brahmin, Megha, throws five lotus flowers to the Buddha; these blossoms miraculously floated over Dipankara's head, as portrayed at the top of the stele. The figure of Megha, the future Śākyamuni, appears again spreading his hair on the ground to protect Buddha Dipankara's feet from the mud. The small Bodhisattva at the lower right is presumably Śākyamuni in his final incarnation. In the plinth appears a representation of the Buddha of the Future, Maitreya. The clumsy proportions of the figure in a canon of five heads to the total height of the image have lost all resemblance to the Graeco-Roman tradition. The flames issuing from the shoulders of the Buddha symbolize the divine radiance emanating from the body of an Enlightened One. This attribute is probably derived from the Iranian concept of the sacred fire as an emblem of Ahura Mazda.

J. 92; AAA 5; MDAFA, x, Pl. x.

48. MAITREYA AND WORSHIPPERS
Schist; h. 9⅞ in. (25 cm.)
KM 61.7.12 (from Pāitāvā)

Like many Gandhāra reliefs of the third century and later, this relief in the hieratic frontal presentation of the figure of Maitreya and donors suggests the orientalized Roman sculpture of Palmyra and Dura Europos.

J. 94; AAA 101; J. Hackin, L'oeuvre de la Délégation Archéologique Française en Afghanistan (1922–32), Tokyo, 1933, fig. 29.

49. FIGURE IN KUSHAN DRESS
Schist; h. 19⅝ in. (50 cm.)
KM 61.7.6 (from Shotorak)

The figure standing under a śal tree and carrying offerings in his hands is probably a donor. He wears the characteristic Kushan mantle, baggy pantaloons, and felt boots familiar in the famous statues of King Kanishka from Surkh Kotal and Mathurā. The figure has the rigid frontality of the Buddha images from the same site, and the drapery folds are reduced to the same formula of string-like ridges. Similar types of donor figures have been found at Hadda (MDFA, xix, Pl. x, fig. 40).

J. 97; AAA 104.

50. HEAD OF BUDDHA
Schist; h. 8⅝ in. (22 cm.)
KM 61.7.1 (from Shotorak)

This head, while retaining certain suggestions of the earlier classical style, is far more Indian than most Gandhāra heads in the distinctly lotiform eyes, the bow-like flaring of the eyebrows, and the orthodox indication of the urna and the usnisa. As in many of the late Gandhāra Buddha images, the rather dry, mask-like quality is suggestive of the sculpture of Palmyra.

I. 140, tav. LIV.

51. BUDDHA WORSHIPPED BY THE THREE KĀŚYAPAS
Schist; 22¾ x 31½ in. (58 x 89 cm.)
KM 64.7.1 (from Shotorak)

The deep pictorial carving of the relief is an illustration of the illusionistic or pictorial mode of Antonine sculpture, notable in many famous pieces of second century Gandhāra sculpture from Pakistan.

The relief shows the three Kāśyapa brothers, each accompanied by a disciple, advancing reverently towards the Buddha after their conversion. At the extreme right are portrait figures of a Kushan noble and his wife, who is dressed in Greek fashion. The Buddha Maitreya flanked by long processions of devotees to right and left appears at the top of the relief. The legend is intended to show the submission of Brahmanism to the Buddha.

MDAFA, x, Pl. xix.

HADDA

Like a golden mirage of towers, the thousand *stupas* of Nagarahāra and Hadda beckoned the Chinese pilgrims Fa Hsien and Hsüan-tsang to worship their famous relics. Both Fa Hsien, writing in the fifth century, and Hsüan-tsang, who visited Afghanistan in the early seventh century, mention the splendid shrines and miracle-working relics in the region of modern Jelalabad. Hadda was apparently still a flourishing center in the seventh century and appears to have escaped the devastation wrought at nearby Nagarahāra, where the Master of the Law remarked, "The *sangharāmas* are many, but the priests are few. The *stupas* are desolate and ruined." Thereafter Hadda sank into oblivion with the coming of the Islamic invaders and remained unnoticed until the nineteenth century, when the great pioneer of Afghan archaeology, Charles Masson, explored its ruinous mounds in search of numismatic treasure. His finds of Roman coins of Domitian, together with issues of the fifth century Emperor Marcian, are among the few positive bits of evidence for the chronology of this site, as well as for its contacts with the West over a period of four centuries. The serious exploration of this site was to wait until 1923, when, with the conclusion of a pact for rights of archaeological excavation, work was begun by the French Archaeological Mission in Afghanistan under the leadership of Foucher and Godard and, later, Charles Barthoux. The efforts of the French archaeologists appear to have been concentrated largely on the *stupa* at Tapa Kalan, a site that yielded some of the more classical examples of sculpture in stone and stucco. The conduct of these excavations was far from scientific, and in their haste to uncover the hundreds of sculptural fragments the archaeologists might as well have been digging potatoes in a field. This enormous amount of material, recovered under very difficult conditions and with the active hostility of the na-

Fig. 6. Head of a Barbarian; Ludovisi Sarcophagus. Second century A.D. Collection of Museo delle Terme, Rome.

tive population, found its way to the Musée Guimet and to the Kabul Museum, the latter possessing no less than thirteen hundred separate objects.

The sculpture of Hadda is comprised of a relatively small number of carvings in schist and soft limestone, and a vast quantity of material in stucco or lime plaster. The stucco sculptures, by reason of the freshness and vivacity of their modeling, immediately appeared to modern critics as a novelty in comparison with the stiff and dry manner of Gandhāra stone sculpture.

The stucco sculpture of Hadda has given rise to a number of theories to explain the striking differences which, superficially at least, appear to exist between the dry, Roman provincial style of Gandhāra stone sculpture and the moving, spiritualized realism of the stucco heads. Sir John Marshall, distinguished for his great work at Taxila, proposed the strange theory that the stucco sculpture represents a late florescence—an "Indo-Afghan Renaissance"—that occurred as much as a century later than the end of the Gandhāra school of stone sculpture. Dr. Bachhofer suggested that the sculpture of Hadda was to be understood as a late baroque development of the Gandhāra style. In these and still other attempts to explain the Hadda style the proponents invariably separate the sculpture in lime plaster from the stone carvings.

The solution to the problems of the style and chronology of Hadda is unfortunately not to be found in any published archaeological reports nor in the various hypotheses mentioned above, but rather in an objective examination of the sculpture itself. The technique of stucco or lime plaster,

Fig. 5. Detail of Vine Scroll, third century A.D. From Leptis Magna.

which predominates at Hadda, was an invention of the late Hellenistic period in Alexandria, where gypsum was first used as a cheap substitute for marble. From there the technique spread to Iran and to India, beginning with the intensified trade relations with the Roman West in the early first century A.D. Sir Mortimer Wheeler has pointed out that stucco heads found at Sabratha in Roman North Africa are hardly to be distinguished in type and technique from examples from Hadda. Stucco appeared as early as the first century A.D. at Taxila, and there is every reason to suppose that it was used as a substitute for, or as an adjunct to, stone carving even before A.D. 241, the period when schist carving seems to have predominated both north and south of the Khyber Pass.

As elsewhere in the Buddhist establishments of Afghanistan and northwest Pakistan, it was customary to mold the bodies of Buddha images and other figures out of local earth covered by a thin layer of gypsum plaster. Following a process originating in Alexandria, the heads of statues and figures in relief were constructed on a rough core of lime plaster mixed with straw and small stones, which was then covered with an outer layer or shell of finer stucco for the modeling of the features and hair. The fragile bodies of the Hadda images had crumbled to dust even before the beginning of modern excavations, and this accounts for the predominance of heads in collections of this material.

The stone carvings of Hadda in schist and in limestone are of particular interest, not only because the motifs and technique correspond to the examples of Gandhāra sculpture in Pakistan, but also because it is in these materials that we find some of the most strikingly classical parallels. These are in the nature of reflections of various styles of Roman relief from the first to the third century A.D. For example, the vine scroll of No. 72 is known in many examples from Gandhāra proper, and its deeply carved, reticulated style relates the whole school to Roman sculpture of the Antonine and Severid periods (Fig. 5). Some of the limestone panels, notably the bacchanalian scene of No. 73, appear to reflect an earlier style. The mode of isolating the figures against a plain background corresponds very closely to Roman reliefs of the late first century A.D. and is also found in a series of Gandhāra reliefs from Buner. These parallels with classical art are also present in the stucco sculpture from Hadda, notably in the many heads of Pergamene type that may well be contemporary reflections of the Antonine revival of the Hellenistic style.

The conclusion to be drawn from these classical parallels is not the invention of either a baroque phase of Gandhāra art or the assumption of an Indo-Afghan renaissance in stucco. The classical types found at Hadda both in stone and stucco include many close resemblances to Hellenistic as well as Roman work from the Flavian to the Severid periods. Their presence can only indicate that, as in Gandhāra stone sculpture, the carvers and stucco workers of Hadda were either trained in Western studios where these models were preserved, or that they had access to actual classical prototypes. In this connection one should perhaps not overlook the possible influence of such material as the classical objects in the treasure of Begrām. It is hardly likely that sculptors working in Afghanistan should have suddenly invented from their own imagination such remarkable counterfeits of Dionysian figures and motifs, as well as Antonine baroque types. Furthermore, the Hadda stuccoes and the related pieces in stone are too close to Late

Hellenistic or Roman originals to make it logical to regard them as any later than the second or third century in date. It is, of course, highly probable that new work was done or old decorations repaired as late as the fifth century in a style that, as in Gandhāra stone sculpture, seems to represent a gradual Indianization of the earlier classical tradition.

From the aesthetic point of view the stucco sculptures from Hadda are admittedly far superior to the rather formalized limestone and schist carvings. As works of art many are comparable to the *bozzetti* of Bernini. The malleable stucco medium afforded a far greater opportunity for freshness and expressiveness in execution. The haunting resemblance of many individual heads to the spiritual realism of Gothic art is not surprising when one considers that many of the qualities of thirteenth century Christian art were already present in the last flowering of the Hellenistic tradition—the Antonine sculpture of the second century A.D. (Fig. 6). It is there that one finds the same pictorial richness of carving reproduced at Hadda and, as in the pathos of the heads of dying barbarians in Roman battle sarcophagi, the same concern for registering inner feeling and emotion through the expressionistic distortion of the facial mask. In these Roman reliefs, as in Roman portraits of the second century and later, we find the same combination of spiritual and physical tumult and agony, ecstasy, and tension that mark the heads of monks and barbarians at Hadda. It is apparent, too, that here was a style that entirely answered the spiritual needs of the followers of mystical Buddhism.

52

The many examples of both stone and stucco sculpture from this famous site near Jelalabad are obviously to be dated in different periods. The earliest and most classical (or late Hellenistic) types are certainly no later than the second or third century. The more conventional Buddha images and other pieces clearly revealing Indian influence were probably made as late as the fifth century of our era.

53

54

58

57

56

61

62

9

63 67

70

71

72

73

52. HEAD OF BUDDHA
  Stucco; h. 9⅞ in. (25 cm.)
  KM 62.3.587   (from Tapa Kalan)

This is one of the most beautiful surviving fragments of Buddha heads from Hadda. There is a strange dichotomy of Indian and classical elements in the soft modeling of certain features such as the lips and the more formalized treatment of the upper part of the face.

J. 107; I. 66, tav. XXVII and cover; AAA 116; MDAFA, VI, fig. 24a.

53. TYCHE
  Limestone; h. 7⅛ x 6¼ in. (18.1 x 15.8 cm.)
  KM 62.3.205

An extraordinary relief, apparently a representation of the city goddess of Hadda, presents her flanked by the mailed figures of a cavalryman and infantryman. At her feet to right and left are tritons, symbols of the confluence of rivers at the ancient site. As in classical representations of tyches, the goddess holds a cornucopia as an attribute. This emblem suggests that her worship in Kushan times was in some way connected with the cult of Ardoksho, an ancient Iranian goddess of fortune whose effigy appears both on Kushan coins and in Gandhāra sculpture. The rigid formality of this relief-composition is strangely suggestive of the style of late Roman consular diptychs and Sasanian sculpture of the third century.

54. HEAD OF A DEMON
  Stucco; h. 3½ in. (9.5 cm.)
  KM 62.3.19   (from Tapa Kalan)

J. 167; AAA 178.

55. HEAD OF A DEMON
  Stucco; h. 3½ in. (9 cm.)
  KM 62.3.20   (from Tapa Kalan)
  (Not illustrated.)

J. 166; AAA 170.

56. HEAD OF A DEMON
  Stucco; h. 4⅛ in. (10.5 cm.)
  KM 62.3.391   (from Tapa Kalan)

J. 168; I. 119 tav. XLVI; MDAFA, VI, fig. 99a; AAA 173.

The many heads of half-human, half-animal demons found at Hadda were parts of large compositions representing the assault of Mara at the time of Śākyamuni's Enlightenment. They have been compared to the gargoyles of French Gothic art. Their animal features, like those of the damned in Michelangelo's Last Judgment, evoke memories of the bestial spirits of Pythagoras. The realistic, dynamic style, imbued with a strange pathos, appears as an adaptation of the turmoil and naturalism of the Hellenistic school of Pergamum to Buddhist needs.

57. DEMON WARRIOR
  Stucco; h. 3⅜ in. (8.7 cm.)
  KM 62.3.1103   (from Tapa Kalan)

This fragment, again, must have formed part of a relief representing the army of Mara. The strange expression of quizzical pathos on the face of the youthful barbarian suggests the realism and intensity of the great battle reliefs of the Antonine period in Rome. The modeling is extremely strong and fresh, with an extraordinary feeling for the quality of the medium.

J. 134; AAA 176.

58. HEAD OF A YOUTH WITH LONG HAIR
  Stucco; h. 3⅜ in. (8.7 cm.)
  KM 62.3.357   (from Bagh-Gaï)

The youthful face with its deeply shadowed eyes, parted lips, and massive cap of hair has a poignant expressiveness and pictorial realism that again suggests the survival of the Scopaic and Pergamene traditions in Roman sculpture of the second century A.D.

J. 133; AAA 138.

59. DEVATĀ HOLDING TRIRATNA
Stucco; h. 10¼ in. (26 cm.)
KM 62.3.32

The figure is represented supporting three stylized lotus disks emblematic of the Three Jewels: The Buddha, the Law, and the Order. This motif is known in one example of Gandhāra stone carving from Loriyan Tangai, generally regarded as one of the earliest sites of Graeco-Buddhist art in Pakistan.

J. 106; AAA 107.

60. BARBARIAN
Stucco; h. 4 in. (10 cm.)
KM 62.3.9

This dynamically expressive head also appears as an evocation from the Hellenistic world of Pergamum. Of special note are the wonderfully expressive characterization of this portrait and the masterful modeling, in impressionistic fashion, of the form and texture of the face.

J. 155; AAA 142.

61. HEAD OF DEVA
Stucco; h. 6⅝ in. (16.8 cm.)
KM 63.3.438   (from Tapa Kalan)

An athlete of the studio of Lysippus is suggested by this beautiful head with its hair formalized in loose ringlets. This is but one more illustration of the proximity of the sculpture of Hadda to the Mediterranean tradition, chronologically as well as stylistically.

MDAFA, VI, fig. 36.

62. PILGRIM
Stucco; diam. 4⅜ in. (11 cm.)
KM 62.3.1115   (from Tapa Kalan)

This unusual object is in the shape of a medallion filled with the bust of a youthful figure holding the pilgrim's staff and alms bowl. The *emblema*-like composition itself is reminiscent of the famous plaster medallions of Begrām.

I. 98, tav. XXXVII; MDAFA, VI, fig. 97e.

63. HEAD OF NOBLEMAN
Stucco; h. 8½ in. (21.5 cm.)
KM 63.3.424   (from Tapa Kalan)

The more classic types of Gandhāra Bodhisattvas in stone resemble this head of a diademed princely personage. Although probably only the head of a bystander in a scene from the life of Buddha, it is characterized by the same individuality found in the more Hellenistic examples of Hadda sculpture.

I. 79; MDAFA, VI, Pl. 30b.

64. HEAD OF BUDDHA
Stucco; h. 13 in. (33 cm.)
KM 63.3.436   (from Tapa Kalan)

This is a typical example of the conventionalized type of Buddha developed at Hadda. Although the softness of modeling in the lips still suggests the naturalistic Hellenic tradition, the face as a whole is a serene and rigid mask which may well have been executed from a mold. The hair, with a massive, crowning *usnisa*, appears as a separate wig, in which the locks are arranged in deeply grooved, symmetrical wavy lines, a decorative abstraction of a naturalistic classical coiffure.

J. 105; I. 67, tav. XXVIII; AAA 113, 114; MDAFA, VI, Pl. 2.

65. STANDING BUDDHA
Stucco; h. 14⅝ in. (37.2 cm.)
KM 63.3.320   (from Bagh-Gaï)

Many examples of standing Buddha images of this type were brought to light in the excavations of the *stupa* at Bagh-Gaï near Hadda. Originally this fragment and companion figures were placed in an arcade suggesting the arrangement of Christ and his Disciples on Early Christian sarcophagi. Of special iconographical interest is the wearing of the *pallium*, a garment adapted for the Buddha image from the dress of the priests of the mystery cults of the Roman Orient who ushered the souls of the dead to the other world. The style of the drapery represented by ridges and incised lines as well as the stocky canon of proportions indicate that the image belongs to the last phase of artistic activity at Hadda, comparable to the late stone sculpture of Pāitāvā and Shotorak. (For a view of the original setting of this and other statues, see J. Hackin, *Archéologie Bouddhique*, fig. 3.) (Not illustrated.)

66. MAN WITH A HELMET
Stucco; h. 4¾ in. (12 cm.)
KM 62.3.371   (from Tapa Kalan)

The warrior is represented wearing a familiar type of Roman helmet such as may also be seen in the famous statue of Pallas Athena, or Roma, in the Central Museum, Lahore. The deeply expressive eyes and parted lips display the passionate emotion of Hellenistic art seen in so many of the Hadda stuccoes. (Not illustrated.)

J. 135; I. 115, tav. XLIV; MDAFA, III, Pl. 104a.

67. HEAD OF A MONK
Stucco; h. 3⅞ in. (9.7 cm.)
KM 62.3.4   (from Tapa Kalan)

An extraordinary fervor of expression animates this head of an ascetic, probably from a large Nirvāna scene. This feeling of spiritual intensity is achieved by the deeply incised lines that frame the eyes and mouth. In their combination of outward realism and inner spirituality, heads like this seem to forecast the characteristics of Gothic art.

J. 129; I. 113, tav. XLIV; AAA 136; MDAFA, VI, Pl. 59c.

68. FIGURE WEARING A FUR COAT
Stucco; h. 5½ in. (13.8 cm.)
KM 62.3.1091   (from Tapa-i-Kafariha)

One of a number of figurines found at Hadda represented wearing what seems to be the prototype of the modern Afghan fur-lined mantle or *pushtin* is seen here. It is difficult to tell whether the child-like figure has its hands concealed in furry sleeves or whether the arms are indeed the legs of an animal skin. The figure was probably an attendant in the army of Mara.

J. 162; AAA 105; MDAFA, VI, Pl. 98e.

69. HEAD OF DEVATĀ
Stucco; h. 2 in. (5 cm.)
KM 62.3.420

This is one of many such heads of diademed personages with features of a classical type that may be identified perhaps as Bodhisattvas or as attendant deities in a scene from the life of Buddha. (Not illustrated.)

70. BUDDHA IN MEDITATION
Stucco; h. 10⅜ in. (26.2 cm.)
KM 63.3.428

A kind of standardized model for the seated Buddha image, this figure is similar to numbers of examples found not only at Hadda, but also at the later site of stucco sculpture in Pakistan. The drapery is represented only by shallow parallel grooves and the hair by a series of shallow holes in the cap-like coiffure.

J. 161; AAA 151.

71. SCENE FROM THE LIFE OF BUDDHA
Limestone; h. 11⅝ in. (29.5 cm.)
KM 63.3.439   (from Tapa Kalan)

This fragment of an unknown subject belongs to a type of Gandhāra relief reflecting the pictorial mode of Roman carving of the Flavian period and later, in which the dramatis personae are represented in a box-like stage, so deeply undercut as to give the illusion of their existence in a spatial ambience. The figure of Vajrapāni at the extreme right was complete when the relief was first discovered. Of special note is the resemblance of the individual heads of the attendant monks to the strongly characterized portraits in stucco (Nos. 60, 67).

J. 101; AAA 107; MDAFA, VI, Pl. 40b.

72. VINE SCROLL
Schist; h. 6¾ in. (17 cm.)
KM 63.3.418

One of the most classical fragments found at Hadda is this inhabited vine pattern, in which we can recognize the figures of a *putto* and a fox, known in many examples of Roman art in the Severid period. Just as in the examples of this motif at Baalbek and Leptis Magna, the figures in their foliate enframement are so deeply undercut that they appear as a reticulated screen against the background. (See B. Rowland, "The Vine-Scroll in Gandhāra," *Artibus Asiae*, XIX, 3-4, 1956, p. 353.)

J. 98; AAA 108; MDAFA, VI, fig. 81.

73. BACCHANALIAN SCENE
Limestone; h. 11⅝ in. (29.5 cm.)
KM 62.3.24

Many examples of this type of relief representing figures of both sexes drinking from bowls or goblets are known in the earliest relief sculptures of Gandhāra proper. The svelte, nude, and semi-clad forms appear like miniature versions of Praxitelean or Lysippic types of statues. The purely Dionysian character of these reliefs is difficult to explain in a Buddhist setting. It is possible that reliefs of this type, perhaps directed to the surviving Greek population, had the ecumencial intention of suggesting that all, including the pagan divinities, were welcomed and enfolded in the Buddhist cult. The style of the carving, with the figures isolated against a plain background, suggests Roman reliefs of the Flavian period. (See B. Rowland, "Gandhāra, Rome, and Mathurā: The Early Relief Style," *Archives of the Chinese Art Society of America*, X, 1956, figs. 1–8.)

J. 100; AAA 106.

KUNDUZ

The stucco sculpture from this site in the region of ancient Bactria represents the northernmost examples of the technique. The style, like that of the statuary of Fondukistan, represents a late baroque development of the Hadda manner and is perhaps to be dated as late as the fifth or sixth century A.D.

74. HEAD OF WOMAN WITH CURLS
Stucco; h. 4⅞ in. (12.5 cm.)
KM 64.15.1

The cursory exploration of this site north of the Hindu Kush, in 1936, brought to light a small collection of sculpture in stucco recalling the pictorial technique of Hadda. The rather wistful refinement and elegance of this little head appears to prophesy the final phase of Buddhist art at Fondukistan and in the seventh century sculpture of Kashmir. (Not illustrated.)

BĀMIYĀN: 75. A Medallion with two birds holding a string of pearls. From Group D.
Painting on clay; diam. 15 inches (38 cm.).

Fig. 7. View of the Bāmiyān Valley with the 120-foot Buddha.

BAMIYAN

"To the northeast of the royal city there is a mountain, on the declivity of which is placed a stone figure of Buddha, erect, in height 140 or 150 feet. Its golden hues sparkle on every side, and its precious ornaments dazzle the eyes by its brightness. To the east of the convent there is a standing figure of Śākya Buddha, made of metallic stone, in height 100 feet."

This is Hsüan-tsang's brief description of Bāmiyān, one of the greatest monastic establishments in Central Asia. A later visitor, Hui Ch'ao, found the monasteries still flourishing in the eighth century. After that, all is silence until the mention of Genghis Khan's biographer that the Mongol archers, pausing from their orgy of massacre in the valley, were unable to reach the head of the colossus with their arrows. There are various references to this famous site by Islamic chroniclers and geographers such as Al Tabari and Yaqut, and in the seventeenth century the Mogul Emperor Aurangzeb bombarded the great Buddha with his field pieces. During the disasters of the First Afghan War of 1840, Lady Sale and Lieutenant Eyre made notes and sketches of the famous caves during their imprisonment, but the credit for the modern rediscovery of this famous site and the restoration of its statuary and wall-painting belongs to the pioneer members of the French Archaeological Mission in Afghanistan.

The Bāmiyān Valley today, as seen from the heights of the ruined city of Shahr-i-Gholghola or to the west from the ravine of Foulādi, presents one of the most dramatic panoramas in all of Asia (Fig. 7). Beyond the Bāmiyān River and the groves of chanar trees which shade the highway and the modern *caravanserai* and village built of mud brick, one catches a glimpse of the tawny sandstone cliff honeycombed with scores of rock-cut sanctuaries and bracketed by the towering niches of the colossal Buddhas. Behind the cliff rise the snow-covered peaks of the Hindu Kush towering to a height of more than 20,000 feet. As is suggested in Hsüan-tsang's account, this vast monastic complex was divided into convents centered around the two gigantic images of Buddha.

The statue at the eastern end, rising to a height of 120 feet, is really a gigantic magnification of a Gandhāra image (Fig. 8). Only the core of the image is shaped from the rock, and the massively pleated drapery, as well as the details of the now ruined head, were modeled from a thick layer of clay covered with a veneer of lime plaster. The paintings that ornament the vault of this Buddha's niche, as well as the decorations of the adjoining caves that are linked by interior staircases, are executed in a provincial Sasanian style. On the soffit of the niche is a gigantic painting of a sun god in his chariot, perhaps intended as a reference to the solar aspect of Buddha, and on the haunches of the vault is a frieze of Buddhas and donors that recall the massive, static forms of Sasanian sculpture.

Of special interest for the present exhibition are

Fig. 9A. Sasanian textile with Boar's Head pattern. Collection of the Museum for Central Asian Antiquties, New Delhi.

Fig. 9B. Sasanian period stucco medallion with Boar's Head. From Damghan. Collection of the Archaeological Museum, Tehran.

Fig. 10. The 175-foot Buddha, Bāmiyān.

the decorations of Group D, one of the complexes of caves immediately to the west of the giant Buddha, now rendered inaccessible by the collapse of the stairs originally cut into the rock. The vestibule of this complex had its ceiling decorated with a painted imitation of Sasanian textiles consisting of medallions, each containing heraldic beast and bird forms such as may be seen in Nos. 75 and 76. The borders of these painted roundels, like the rare surviving examples of actual Sasanian silks (Fig. 9A), are filled with pearls separated by four cabochons. As in actual examples of silk-weaving, the beasts' forms, like the magnificently stylized boar's head, are presented with a kind of heraldic simplification that illustrates the inimitable Iranian sensibility for abstractly decorative form, a tradition going back to the great ornamental art of Achaemenid times.

Bāmiyān, set in its emerald pocket between the Hindu Kush and the Koh-i-Baba, is located in western Central Asia in the watershed of the Oxus. The Sasanian paintings that decorate its grottoes may be regarded as belonging to a zone of eastern Iranian art that includes the centers of Sasanian art in Russian Central Asia at Varaksha, Pyandhzikent, and Balalik Teppe, and that extends southward to include the Afghan sites of Dokhtar-i-Nōshirwān and Bāmiyān. Although the 120-foot colossus suggests the style of Gandhāra Buddha images of the early second century A.D., the cycle of Sasanian wall-paintings decorating its niche belongs to the period of the Iranian domination of Afghanistan after A.D. 241, and may well be as late as the period of Hephthalite supremacy beginning in the fifth century.

At the foot of the cliff, somewhat to the east of the 120-foot Buddha, Hackin and his associates excavated the debris of a small rock-cut sanctuary which had been completely buried by the falling of a great mass of rocks from the face of the cliff. Cave G (as it was designated) was originally roofed by a carved facsimile of a cupola on squinches. It enclosed a small *stupa*, and the decoration consisted of a combination of sculptured groups and wall-paintings used in conjunction to produce the effect of an illusionistic tableau.

The clay sculpture from this cave, as well as the scant fragments of wall-painting, were parts of a composition representing the Nirvāna of Buddha. The sculptured portions of the composition were originally placed in front of the parts painted on the wall as an illusionistic extension of the sculptural design, and mark the beginning of a style represented in various Central Asian sites. Very elaborate arrangements of such pictorial and plastic elements exist in the grottoes of Tun-hüang. The final development of this type of decoration is to be seen in the famous groups of clay sculpture at the base of the pagoda of Hōryūji at Nara, where the painted background has been replaced by a setting molded in clay. Although reminiscent of the Hadda style, the individual heads from Cave G, like the *devatā* with a heavy crown and the *yaksha* with flaming hair (Nos. 78 and 80), already show that reduction of the face to a decorative mask—extremely hard and dry in modeling—that is characteristic of Buddhist sculpture at Tumshuk and Shorchuk in Chinese Turkestan. A fragment of wall-painting in the Kabul Museum (not included in this exhibition) with the strangely ferocious head of a monk, perhaps Mahākāśyapa, is executed in a wiry draughtsmanship that again suggests the style of painting which flourished in the fifth century and later in Central Asia. Although these remains were originally dated as early as the third century, it seems evident that they belong to the same period as the Sasanian decorations in the complex of the 120-foot Buddha.

The 175-foot Buddha (Fig. 10), housed in a gigantic trefoil niche at the western end of the valley, is an enlargement of an Indian Buddha statue of the Gupta period. The drapery, molded in string-like ridges, reflects the style of the fifth century Buddhas of Mathurā, and the fragments of wall-paintings which cling to the sides of the niche and

Fig. 8. The 120-foot Buddha, Bāmiyān.

the soffit of the vault are a provincial version of the style of the Indian wall-paintings of Ajantā. A number of rock-cut chapels open from an ambulatory behind the feet of the colossus. One of these, No. XI, has a deeply molded, coffered decoration in its cupola, recalling the decoration of the temple of Bacchus at Baalbek. Cave V, from which the decorations in the present exhibition come (Nos. 81, 82), had the drum of the rock-cut cupola ornamented with parallelograms enclosing reliefs of leogryphs, *hamsa* or sacred geese, and *rinceaux* patterns. All of these ornaments are probably no earlier than the sixth century A.D. and represent a syncretic survival of motifs originally classical, Iranian, and Indian.

It should be noted, in closing, that not only are there many elements in the Sasanian cycle of paintings around the niche of the 120-foot Buddha which suggest a dating in the period of Hephthalite domination in the sixth and seventh centuries, but also that many stylistic resemblances can be noted between both the Indian and Iranian paintings at Bāmiyān and the decorations of the seventh century monastery of Fondukistan. These will be discussed later. In other words, it might be possible to conclude that the works both in the Indian and Sasanian manner at this famous site were completed only a short time before the visit of Hsüan-tsang in the early seventh century.

At Kakrak, some two or three miles southeast of the cliff of the giant Buddhas, beyond the ruins of the ghost city of Shahr-i-Gholghola, is another series of cave temples grouped around a rock-cut colossus that is over 40 feet in height. The paintings, removed to the Kabul Museum, are the decorations of the drums and cupolas of the cave sanctuaries. A perfect and complete example is included in the present exhibition (No. 77). It is in the form of a *mandala* or magic diagram. In the center is a Buddha, perhaps Vairocana, with his hands in the Dharma-

cakra *mudrā*, surrounded by a galaxy of smaller Buddhas in circles tangent to the inner enclosure. This is one of the earliest representations of the Mahāyāna Buddhist concept of one of the celestial Buddhas surrounded by his magic emanations which, in ever more elaborate form, become part of the paraphernalia of Vajrayāna Buddhism in Tibet and Nepal and of the Shingon sect in Japan.

These Tantric elements in the Kakrak murals are of special interest in view of the fact that, according to Dr. Edward Conze, Vajrayāna Buddhism originated in the Gandhāra region as early as A.D. 600. Certain details in the Kakrak paintings, like the diadem with the triple crescent worn by a donor known as the Hunter King in the Kabul Museum, resemble the crowns seen in the coins of the Hephthalite rulers of the fifth and sixth centuries. Such a date is supported by the style of the paintings themselves. The Buddhas still retain the massive, inflated forms of the Sasanian figures at Bāmiyān. The conventionalization of the faces into perfect ovoids and the lotiform eyes reflect the canon for Buddhist imagery already formulated in the Gupta period. The stylization of these Buddha figures already suggests the hieratic forms of the art of esoteric Buddhism in Tibet and Nepal. This resemblance to Lamaistic art extends to the attenuated *stupas* that appear in the spandrels between the circles of the *mandala* and to the predilection for a palette of dull reds, earth yellows, and neutralized blues. Many features of the Kakrak Buddha images, such as the spidery fingers posed in the mystic *mudrās*, the masklike faces with their exaggerated arching brows, and the bulky proportions of the bodies, suggest the canons of the last phase of Buddhist art in India, as seen in the statuary and illuminated palm-leaf *sutras* of the Pāla period. These are the characteristics that, with little change, were adopted into the traditions of Buddhist art in Nepal and Tibet.

76

The fragments of paintings in a Sasanian style from this famous monastic center must be dated after the conquest of Shāpur I in A.D. 241 and may be as late as the seventh century A.D. The sculpture and painting from Cave G., with their resemblances to the art of Central Asia, are no earlier than the sixth or seventh century of our era.

BĀMIYĀN: 77. *Mandala*. From Kakrak. Painting on clay; diam. 36¼ inches (98 cm.).

78

80   79

75. MEDALLION WITH TWO BIRDS HOLDING A STRING OF PEARLS
Painting on clay; diam. 15 in. (38 cm.)
KM 61.5.9   (from Group D)

The roundel, with its border filled with pearls separated by four cabuchons, is a standard pattern in Sasanian textile design. It has been suggested that representations of birds with necklaces of pearls, which also occur in copies of Sasanian textiles in Central Asian wall-paintings (Herzfeld, *Am Tor von Asien*, Pl. LXIII), had some connection with the Iranian legend of the bird Varagan and its quest of Light Khvarenah in the form of a pearl in the depths of the sea. The arabic chronicler Yaqut noted that there were paintings at Bāmiyān "representing all the birds created by God." Another example of this iconography, but with a single dove, from Group D at Bāmiyān is reproduced in Rowland, "Sasanian Paintings at Bāmiyān," *Bulletin of the Iranian Institute*, Vol. VI, p. 39, fig. 5.

J. 178; AAA 8.

76. MEDALLION WITH BOAR'S HEAD
Painting on clay; diam. 12⅜ in. (31.5 cm.)
KM 61.5.12   (from Group D)

The motif of the boar's head occurs in the sculptural decoration of the palace at Damghan, in the great grotto of Taq-i-Bustan, as well as in actual examples of Sasanian silks and other painted copies of this design in Central Asian wall-paintings. (Herzfeld, *Am Tor von Asien*, Pl. LXIV, and Ghirshman, *Persian Art*, 281.) This motif appears to have had a special connection with the Sasanian Emperor Khusrau II (A.D. 590–628), although many earlier examples are known. This device was an emblem of the Sasanian god of victory, Verathragna.

J. 179; AAA 182; MDAFA, II, Pl X and LXXXIV, fig. 102.

77. MANDALA
Painting on clay; diam. 36¼ in. (98 cm.)
KM 61.5.1   (from Kakrak)

This is a decoration from the dome of one of the multiple chapels of Kakrak, probably one of the earliest known examples of a cosmic *mandala* or diagram. The central Buddha with his hands in Dharmacakra *mudrā* is perhaps to be identified as Vairocana, surrounded by a constellation of smaller Buddhas in Dhyāni *mudrā*, who are his miraculous emanations. Both the iconography and the color scheme in subdued reds, browns, ochres, and blues anticipate the esoteric painting in Tibet and Nepal.

J. 180; I. 145, tav. LVI; AAA 8; MDAFA, III, fig. 184.

78. HEAD OF DEVATĀ
Painted clay; h. 5¼ in. (13.4 cm.)
KM 61.5.3   (from Cave G)

This and a number of other heads from Cave G at Bāmiyān probably form parts of a representation of the Nirvāna, executed partly in sculpture, partly in painting. Although the decorations of Cave G were originally dated as early as the third century, there are many indications that both painting and sculpture belong to the very end of the artistic activity at Bāmiyān. Both the material and the pictorial modeling suggest the seventh century sculpture of Fondukistan.

J. 181; AAA 180.

79. HEAD OF A MONK
Painted clay; h. 4⅞ in. (12.5 cm.)
KM 61.5.10   (from Cave G)

The formalization of the head in rounded volumes and the indication of certain features by painting rather than modeling anticipate the sculptural technique of many sites in Central Asia. Like the heads of mourners in the painting complementing the statuary in a tableau of the Nirvāna (I. 147; MDAFA, III, 51)—unfortunately unavailable for this exhibition—the face is a formalized mask expressing the incredulity and grief of the Buddha's follower at the bier of the Tathāgata.

J. 182; AAA 185.

80. HEAD OF A YAKSHA
   Painted clay; h. 5⅜ in. (13.7 cm.)
   KM 61.5.11   (from Cave G)

One of the minor divinities present at the death of the Buddha is represented here. The mask, convulsed in a paroxysm of anguish, is basically reminiscent of the bestial satyrs of classical antiquity. The flaming hair anticipates the representations of the guardian deities of medieval Japan, such as the famous Juni Shinshō of Shinyakushiji at Nara.

J. 183; AAA 184.

81. WINGED LEOGRYPH
   Stucco; h. 11 in. (28 cm.)
   KM 61.5.7   (from Cave V)

This panel in the shape of a parallelogram was part of the decoration of the dome of one of the rock-cut sanctuaries near the 175-foot Buddha. This motif of ultimately classical origin is related to the form seen in the famous Begrām ivory, No. 40. The stylization of the animal suggests the heraldic beasts of Sasanian sculpture and textiles.

J. 184; AAA 183.

82. FOLIATE SCROLL   (from Cave V)
   Stucco; h. 8¼ in. (21 cm.)
   KM 61.5.8

Like its counterparts in stone at Hadda (No. 72), this deeply modeled, spiraling vine scroll is reminiscent of Roman architectural ornaments of the second century A.D. and later. The resemblance of this *rinçeau* to similar decorations at Fondukistan suggest a date as late as the sixth or seventh century.

J. 185; AAA 181.

KABUL

In the days of Buddhist supremacy the modern capital of Afghanistan was the center of a number of Buddhist establishments that were stepping-stones for the pilgrim between the kingdom of Kāpiśa and Nagarahāra. These would include the ruinous *stupa* of Shevaki in the shadow of the Chakri Hills, the Buddhist pillar or *minar* that crowns this eminence, and, in a barren defile of Logar Valley, the ruined *stupa* of Guldāra.

In the shadow of the tomb of Nadir Shah in the eastern outskirts of Kabul lie the crumbling remains of the monastery of Teppe Marandjān, excavated by the French Mission in the decade before the War. The figure of a kneeling donor from this site (No. 83), included in the present exhibition, is part of a collection of clay sculpture that may be dated in the late fourth century by the find of a hoard of Sasanian coins. The statues of Buddhas and Bodhisattvas discovered in an almost perfect state of preservation are a local variant of the later, more Indian type of sculpture at Hadda. These images were modeled in local clay, replacing stucco, and were arranged in painted niches. These little religious stage tableaux containing painting and sculpture mark the beginning of an illusionistic technique continued at Bāmiyān, Fondukistan, and throughout all of Central Asia.

Teppe Khazana, not far from Kabul, has yielded a few fragments of clay sculpture that appear to be related to the final baroque development, in the fifth or sixth century A.D., of the Gandhāra style at Fondukistan (Nos. 84 and 85). A few examples of stone sculpture from nearby Tagao presumably belong to the same school that produced the schist carvings in the region of Begrām. The head of a fasting Buddha (No. 87) is a repetition of a type known in a number of remarkable examples of Gandhāra sculpture in the museums of Peshawar and Lahore.

Kotal Khair Khaneh is a little eminence in the pass that separates Kabul from the vale of Kāpiśa. This was the site of a temple dedicated, not to Buddhism, but to an Iranian cult which included a solar deity, either Sūrya or Mithra. The best preserved cult image carved in white marble portrays the sun god, dressed in Iranian costume, riding in a two-horse chariot and accompanied by two attendants who may be identified as the descendants of the Dioscuroi, Sūrya's acolytes Danda and Pingala (No. 86). The rather hieratic frontal conception as well as the heavy proportions of the figures and their costumes are reminiscent of Sasanian art, and it is certain the shrine and its statuary date from the period after the Persian conquest of 241. This dating is confirmed by the resemblance of details of dress and diadems to the robes and crowns of the Sasanian rulers of the fourth century.

What are probably the last examples of pre-Islamic sculpture in Afghanistan are a group of Brahmanical marble carvings that have come to light at Tagao and Gardez during the last thirty years. None of these objects was recovered by scientific excavation but all appear to have been cult images in a Saivite temple. These include a head of Śiva from Gardez (No. 89) which was in the Kabul Museum as early as 1936, a smaller head of Durgā from Tagao (No. 88), and, a more recent find, a complicated relief of Durgā overcoming Mahisāsura. Another version of this latter theme is now in the Museo Nazionale d'Arte Orientale in Rome. All are clearly provincial examples of a post-Gupta style, dating from the seventh or eighth century when large parts of Afghanistan were under the rule of Hindu Shahis. The head of Śiva, with a lunar symbol in the crown, is a benign mask conceived in abstract swelling planes, suggestive at once of some of the heads of deities in the seventh and eighth century sculpture of the Deccan. The spheroidal conception of the head and its feeling of fullness suggests certain heads of the T'ang period in China. The same is true of the smaller head of

Durgā, notable especially for the delicate and intricate carving of the headdress. The two reliefs of the embattled goddess are like miniature versions of some of the more dynamic cave sculptures of western India. This is a completely Indian style that has nothing to do with the marble carvings from Khair Khaneh nor the Indo-Iranian manner of Fondukistan.

88

84

87

85

TEPPE MARANDJĀN

83. KNEELING DONOR
Clay; h. 11¼ in. (28.5 cm.)
KM 64.11.7

The site of this monastery on the eastern outskirts of Kabul may be dated in the late fourth century by the find of a hoard of coins of Kushano-Sasanian rulers and issues of Shāpur II (310–379) and Shāpur III (385–388). The sculpture, executed in clay with a thin veneer of lime plaster, appears as a later development of the Hadda style, anticipating the style of Cave G at Bāmiyān and the art of Fondukistan. (Not illustrated.)

MDAFA, VIII, fig. 10.

TEPPE KHAZANA

84. HEAD OF A CHILD
Terra cotta; h. 2½ in. (6.5 cm.)
KM 63.11.2

The fragments from this site in the environs of Kabul illustrate the last phase of Buddhist art in Afghanistan of the fifth or sixth century A.D. These heads, like the clay figures from Fondukistan, are strongly suggestive of Gupta sculpture in India.

J. 172; AAA 186.

85. HEAD OF A BODHISATTVA
Terra cotta; h. 4⅜ in. (11 cm.)
KM 63.11.1

J. 173; AAA 187.

KOTAL KHAIR KHANEH

86. SŪRYA
White marble; h. 12½ in. (32 cm.)
KM 63.21.1

A representation of Sūrya in his chariot, half Sasanian, half Kushan in style, has many parallels in Indian art, including a relief on the railing of Bodh Gayā (Rowland, *Art and Architecture of India*, Pl. 19A). The attendants Danda and Pingala are, like

Sūrya, dressed in Sasanian costume. They may be ultimately derived from the attendants of Palmyrene gods and the Dioscuroi of Greek mythology. This image was a cult statue in a sanctuary dedicated to the worship of the sun god. Like the fire temple at Surkh Kotal, this shrine reminds us once again of the completely syncretic nature of the Kushan pantheon. It is on this very hill that the festival inaugurating the beginning of spring is celebrated by the Afghans to the present day.

J. 176; AAA 190; MDAFA, VII, Pls. XI–XIII.

TAGAO

87. HEAD OF A FASTING BUDDHA
Schist; h. 8¼ in. (21.1 cm.)
KM 64.23.5   (from Najrab)

This is the head of a statue that must have resembled the famous ascetic Buddha of the Lahore Museum, which represents Śākyamuni reduced to a veritable skeleton as a result of the austerities practised before his attainment of Enlightenment. This variety of brutal realism, in which, as in the present example, the head is represented as a skull covered by the tightly stretched skin, stems directly from the morbidly realistic art of the late Hellenistic period in Alexandria, as represented notably by the famous statuette of an invalid (Winifred Lamb, *Greek and Roman Bronzes*, London, 1929, Pl. LXXVIIA).

88. HEAD OF DURGĀ
White marble; h. 5 in. (12.7 cm.)
KM 63.23.3

This is one of a group of marbles that have come to light at Tagao and Gardez, which apparently represent the last phase of pre-Islamic art in Afghanistan. The head of Durgā, the terrible form of Śiva's consort Parvatī, appears to be a provincial example of a post-Gupta style and, like the head of Śiva from Gardez (No. 89), has affinities with the seventh and eighth century sculpture of Kashmir.

J. 177; AAA 194.

GARDEZ

89. HEAD OF ŚIVA
   White marble; h. 10 in. (25.5 cm.)
   KM 64.25.1

One of a small group of marble sculptures dedicated
to a Saivite cult, this head together with the mask
of Durgā (No. 88) is probably no earlier than the
seventh or eighth century in date. The head may
be identified as Śiva by the attribute of the lunar
crescent in the crown. Like the Durgā from Tagao,
this marble fragment recalls the heads of Hindu
deities in the sculpture of the seventh century and
later in the Deccan and, at the same time, its composition in smooth, rounded planes suggests the
art of the T'ang period in China. (Not illustrated.)

FONDUKISTAN: 93. Bust of a *devatā*. Painted clay; h. 11¼ inches (28.5 cm.).

FONDUKISTAN

Beyond Charikar the highway to the north enters the defiles of the Ghorband River, moving through narrow canyons and over the rolling green meadows on the valley floor. The villages are few and far between in the Ghorband Valley, and all have their *caravanserai* built like miniature Carcassonnes in mud brick with crenellated towers and curtain walls. At certain seasons of the year one may encounter tribes like the Hazaras with their camels and flocks, but generally the dusty road is clogged with buses and oil trucks moving towards the passes that lead to the north and the Russian frontier. It was in the hills overlooking the Ghorband Valley that the French Archaeological Mission made one of the most notable discoveries in Central Asian art—the monastery of Fondukistan.

As early as 1936 a number of baked clay images uncovered by the spring floods had been brought to the Kabul Museum, and the excavations resulting from these random finds uncovered one of the most significant monuments for the history of Buddhist art in western Turkestan. The finding of a hoard of coins including issues of the Hephthalite rulers and of Khusrau II of Iran (590–628) might make it possible to date this site in the seventh century, but, since these moneys were in the form of an offering, the founding of the monastery may be placed in a somewhat earlier period.

The plan of the monastery, set on a conaic hill at Fondukistan, follows that of other religious establishments throughout Gandhāra and Afghanistan in its arrangement in a series of courtyards surrounded by niches containing ensembles of sculptured figures. These little chapels at Fondukistan were filled with groups of clay images supplemented by gaily painted backgrounds, which may well have represented the celestial assemblies of one of the Paradise *sūtras* or portrayals of *mandalas* with effigies of the divine Buddhas and their attendant Bodhisattvas.

Fig. 11A. Bodhisattva. From Fondukistan. Collection of the Kabul Museum.

ʒ. 11B. Wall-painting of Avalokiteśvara. From Fon-
kistan. Collection of the Kabul Museum.

This illusionistic combination of painting and
sculpture, already studied in Cave G at Bāmiyān,
is the beginning of a style designed to create a
baroque illusion of forms in a stage space; its final
development is reached in the elaborate combina-
tions of sculptured figures and painted backgrounds
that we find in the Thousand Buddha caves at Tun-
huang. The sculpture of Fondukistan also illustrates
the beginning of a new technique destined to spread
throughout Central Asia and China, the employ-
ment of lightly baked clay as a substitute for the
stucco universally used at Hadda and elsewhere in
earlier centuries.

The wall-paintings of Fondukistan reflect both
the Sasanian and the Indian styles at Bāmiyān, and
the individual figures of Taras or Bodhisattvas offer
close parallels to similar forms in the fifth and sixth
century murals at Ajantā. The painted clay statues
of donors still retain echoes of Sasanian art in their
heavy proportions and details of dress. But it is in
the beautiful statues of Bodhisattvas and *devatās* of
Fondukistan (Nos. 92, 93 and Fig. 11A) that we see
the emergence of a new style that might be described as a mannerist development of the refinement of Gupta art. This style retains the pictorial
character of the Hadda stuccoes, but the mood has
changed. The figures have an exaggerated, attenuated elegance. The exquisite gestures of their hands
complement the soft beauty of the swaying bodies,
the faces lost in the expression of a sort of sensuous,
inner reverie. These divinities are possessed by a
feeling of languid hauteur, and their rarefied grace
of pose and expression is heightened further by the
precise beauty of the separately modeled necklaces
and diadems.

This is a formula which the artists of Fondukistan
must have found peculiarly effective for expressing
the demand for images which, following the nature
of Mahāyāna literature, should be both sensuous
and other-worldly. These images have an air of
individuality within a spiritual state, just as, in the
devotional sects of Buddhism and Hinduism, the

individual soul retains its identity even in the bliss of union with the divine. This elegant style, already suggested in certain sculptures from Teppe Marandjān and Kamadaka (Nos. 90, 91), is reflected in the clay reliefs of Central Asian sites like Tumschuk and Shorchuk, and its last metamorphosis may be seen in the painted clay statues of the T'ang period at Tun-hüang. Many of the fragments found at Fondukistan are so nearly identical in style with the seventh century sculpture of Kashmir, notably the heads of Bodhisattvas and *devatās* from Ushkur, that the art of these two sites appears as part of the same peripheral Buddhist culture that survived beyond the boundaries of India at a time when this religion, and its art, were slowly dying out in the land of its origin. Fondukistan represents the final and most delicate flowering of Buddhist art in Afghanistan and the transformation of an originally Indian manner into a true Central Asian style.

94

The painted clay sculpture from this monastery overlooking the Ghorband Valley may
be dated in the seventh century A.D. or earlier. This chronology is based not only on the
post-Gupta style of the statuary, but also on the finds of coins of the Hephthalite kings
and the Sasanian Khusrau II (590–628).

96

95

90

91

The stucco heads from Kamadaka are close to the last style of Buddhist sculpture at Fondukistan and are probably to be dated in the seventh century.

KAMADAKA

90. HEAD OF BUDDHA
Stucco; h. 13¾ in. (35 cm.)
KM 63.23.1

Although suggestive of some of the Buddha heads of Hadda, the softer, more elegant and pictorial modeling of the present example anticipates the late sculpture of Fondukistan.

J. 174; AAA 189.

91. HEAD OF DEVATĀ
Stucco; h. 5 in. (12.7 cm.)
KM 63.23.2

This head again appears as a belated rococo version of the Hadda style.

J. 175; AAA 188.

FONDUKISTAN

92. BUST OF DEVA
Painted clay; h. 11¾ in. (30 cm.)
KM 61.9.6

This figure originally formed part of a group of images, perhaps representing a Buddhist Paradise or *mandala*, in one of the niches of the monastery. The material is lightly baked clay with traces of polychromy. This image and the *devatā* No. 93 illustrate the graceful mannerist mode which evolved in this last known stronghold of Buddhism in Afghanistan.

J. 187; AAA 191; MDAFA, VIII, fig. 154.

93. BUST OF DEVATĀ
Painted clay; h. 11¼ in. (28.5 cm.)
KM 61.9.1

The extraordinarily elongated canon of proportion is a mannered outgrowth of the Gupta ideal. Typical of this late art is the combination of soft sensuality and a kind of world-weary grace. Like all the sculpture from this site the statue was originally brilliantly painted but only slight traces of the red underpainting survive. Terra cotta molds used for pressing relief statues in wet clay have been found at the Central Asian sites of Shorchuk and Tumschuk, and it may be that a similar method was employed at Fondukistan.

J. 186; AAA 10; MDAFA, VIII, figs. 150, 152; I. 149, tav. LVII.

94. MASK OF A DEMON
Painted clay; h. 7½ in. (19 cm.)
KM 61.9.2

The "Gorgon" mask wreathed in vines is a possible prototype for the Kirtimukha of Indian art. The fragment and its foliate enframement—undoubtedly executed with molds—is close to the stucco decorations of Cave V at Bāmiyān (No. 82).

J. 188; I. 152, tav. LIX; AAA 179; MDAFA, VIII, fig. 162.

95. HEAD OF A BEARDED MAN
Painted clay; h. 6½ in. (16.5 cm.)
KM 61.9.3

Probably this fragment may be identified as the head of a donor. Like all the sculpture of Fondukistan, it appears as a more animated, fluid development from the technique of Hadda.

J. 189; I. 150, tav. LVIII; AAA 193; MDAFA, VIII, figs. 183, 184.

96. HEAD OF A BOY IN A CONICAL CAP
Painted clay; h. 4⅛ in. (10.5 cm.)
KM 61.9.4

The head of this little boy with his heavy lids and thick lips suggests the appearance of the Tajik and Hazara shepherd lads encountered in the Ghorband and Bāmiyān Valleys today.

J. 190; I. 151, tav. LVIII; AAA 192; MDAFA, VIII, fig. 186.

BACTRIANA

Fig. 13. Statue of a Kushan Prince. From Surkh Kotal. Collection of the Kabul Museum.

Northern Afghanistan, stretching from the Hindu Kush to the Amu Darya or Oxus River, comprised the ancient domain of the Bactrian kings, the successors of Alexander, who maintained a citadel of Hellenism in the very heart of Asia until they were overwhelmed by an invasion of the barbarian Sakas in 140 B.C. The recent French excavations near Khodjagan on the south bank of the Oxus are bringing to light the ruins of a Graeco-Bactrian city, but beyond this the only remnants of this period of Greek rule in Afghanistan are the magnificent series of coins issued by the founder of the line, Diodotus, and his successors. One of the great treasures of the Kabul Museum is the hoard of Bactrian coins unearthed at Kunduz, which includes magnificent examples, many of them unique, of this line of Hellenistic sovereigns (Fig. 12).

In the first century B.C. the Bactrian realm became the heartland of the Kushanas, the Yüeh-chih of the Chinese histories of the Han period, who, after a migration that had taken them over Central Asia, became the founders of a great empire that within one hundred years was to include vast territories of northern Pakistan and India. One of the most dramatic archaeological discoveries of our century was the excavation at Surkh Kotal of what might be designated as a Kushan national shrine. This great architectural complex, enclosing a natural hill in a series of sanctuaries, recalls the famous Seleucid memorial of Nimrud Dagh. It included a fire temple and a fire altar dedicated to the sacred fire of the Kushan emperors, a Kushan version of the Mazdaean temples of Parthian Iran. A separate precinct was reserved for cult images of the great rulers of the Kushan dynasty. An inscription in the Greek alphabet, used to transcribe the Kushan or Bactrian language, records the dedication of this templed hill to the Kushan genius of victory under its greatest ruler, Kanishka.

Although the impressive portrait statues of Kanishka and other princes of the line (Fig. 13) could
not be imported for the present exhibition, a single
fragment of sculpture from Chamqala (No. 97)
can serve to give some idea of the character of
Kushan-Bactrian sculpture of the late first or early
second century A.D. This architectural fragment,
which came to light at a site not far from Kunduz,
is a capital, presumably from a Buddhist monu-
ment. This is a form of capital basically derived
from the Persepolitan type of Achaemenid times.
It is comprised of addorsed, winged gryphons above
a torus of interlaced foliage, enclosed between two
rings supported by modillions. The material, like
that of the Imperial statues from Surkh Kotal, is a
yellowish limestone, and the capital as a whole
bears a resemblance to Indo-Persian capitals oc-
casionally seen in Gandhāra sculpture.

As Daniel Schlumberger, director of the excavations at Surkh Kotal, has pointed out, there is nothing remotely Hellenic about the plan of this complex; rather its completely rectilinear arrangement
in a series of platforms recalls both ancient Mesopotamian citadels and the Achaemenid palaces of
Persepolis. Certain other reliefs from Chamqala
with representations of scenes from the life of Buddha reveal an obvious relationship to the sculptural
style of Gandhāra. At the present state of our knowl-
edge, it is impossible to state categorically whether
these carvings are northern provincial reflections
of the Indo-Roman school of northwest Pakistan
or if indeed they represent the beginnings of a style
that grew out of a now lost school of Hellenistic
art in Bactria.

Fig. 12. Coin (double decadrachma) of Amyntas. From
the Kunduz hoard. Obverse. Reverse.

97

The limestone reliefs and capitals from this site near the famous Kushan sanctuary of Surkh Kotal are northern examples of the Gandhāra style of stone sculpture and may be dated in the second or third century A.D.

CHAMQALA (BAGHLAN)

97. GRYPHON CAPITAL
Limestone; h. 10⅝ in. (27 cm.)
KM 64.13.1

This fragment, together with other capitals and reliefs found at a site not far from Surkh Kotal, was part of a Buddhist sanctuary in the very heart of the Kushan realm. This capital was evidently the crowning member of a column of the Indo-Persian type, such as is frequently seen in Gandhāra reliefs. The base of the capital consists of a torus of stylized plaited foliage between two circular bands with modillions. Above are addorsed gryphons with wings and horns. A frontal leonine mask appears between the animals. Both the form of this animal capital and such details as the horns and scimitar-like wings are reminiscent of the Persepolitan capitals of Achaemenid times.

MDAFA, XIX, Pl. XXV, 1, 2.

THE ART OF THE GHAZNAVID EMPIRE

Ghazni, the former capital of one of the great empires of the Islamic world, is now a vast field of ruins on the dusty plain between Kabul and Kandahar. It may be recalled that Ghazni in ancient times was the capital of the province of Arachosia, conquered by Alexander and later by his Bactrian successor Demetrius. A Greek inscription of the famous Buddhist Emperor Aśoka has recently been found not far from Kandahar. To the northeast of the modern town rise the stumps of the giant minarets that were once the pride of the capital raised by Ghazni's greatest ruler, Mahmud the Idol-smasher. Mahmud's reign in the early eleventh century marked the climax in the development of an empire that had been founded by Alptagin in 961. Mahmud is remembered for his many expeditions into India, which completely shattered the social structure of the Hindu world of northern India, culminating with his campaign of 1025 against Rajasthan that ended with the sack of the famous sun temple at Somnath.

A few years later Mahmud became master of all Iran. In the midst of his endless military enterprises this sovereign transformed Ghazni into a capital that was the splendor of the Islamic world. His court was graced by such great Iranian literary figures as the poet Firdausi and the historian Al-Beruni. The decline of Ghaznavid power began with the death of Mahmud, and the grandeur of Mahmud's capital perished in flames when the city fell to Ali-ud-Din the Ghurid, known as "the incendiary of the world." The brief revival of culture which followed this catastrophe ended with the total destruction wrought by the Mongols in A.D. 1221.

The model for the splendors of the Ghaznavid capital was Baghdad of the Abbasid caliphate, a civilization to which Ghazni, like all the Arab world, acknowledged an artistic as well as a political indebtedness. Ghaznavid civilization, as revealed in literature and in the fragments of its art, is a fusion of Arab and Iranian elements. The Ghaznavid rulers, like the Moguls in India, had a preference for the exquisite refinements of Persian art and for the poetry of the Persian language. As did the Moguls, who employed artists from every corner of the Islamic world, Mahmud and his successors imported craftsmen from Iran and the Persian realms beyond the Oxus. It is not surprising, therefore, that Ghaznavid art should reveal an eclectic character with the principal influences coming from conquered Iran.

At Lashkari Bazaar, not far from Ghazni, is the site of a palace of the Ghaznavid kings, a pleasure park and hunting lodge built for Mas'ud I (1031–40) who was renowned for his prowess in the chase. This structure was modeled on Abbasid palaces, and the arrangement of its living quarters, courts, and seraglio goes back to more ancient royal dwellings of the pre-Islamic period.

The Islamic collections of the Kabul Museum include a number of marble reliefs that have come to light in the Ghazni area within the last decade. Although it has become impossible to attach these random discoveries to definite sites, they must belong to the great period of Ghaznavid culture in the eleventh century. The subjects of many of these marble reliefs are like apparitions from ancient Iranian art of the pre–Islamic period. The magnificent representation of a walking lion (No. 98), in its combination of heraldic formality and suggestion of vitality in movement, recalls the animal forms of Sasanian rock carving and metalwork. Even more surprising is a relief with a representation of a mounted hunter attacked by a lion (No. 99). This relief might at first glance be mistaken for a Sasanian portrayal of one of the exploits of Bahram Gur. Hunting scenes like this were the favorite subjects for the decoration of the silver and gold salvers of the Sasanian kings. Their heroic themes, perpetuated in the metalwork of Iran of the Islamic period, make their final appearance in the imperial art of the Ghaznavids.

The collection of material from Ghazni and Lashkari Bazaar in the Kabul Museum also includes a great number of metal objects: ewers, bowls, lampstands, incense burners, and stirrups (Nos. 103–109). The exact provenience of these objects is not known, and it is only possible to conjecture that these artifacts were imported from Herat, Merv, or Nishapur, all celebrated as centers of metalwork in the twelfth century. Some of these vessels with an encrusted or inlay technique may have originated in eastern Iran or Khorasan. The shapes of some of the ewers perpetuate elegant forms developed in Sasanian times (No. 109).

Most of the finds from Ghazni in the Kabul collection were recovered by the Italian expedition of 1957–58 in the palace area of Dast-i-Manara and in a villa site in the Rauza Hills. Among the remarkable finds in the royal hunting box at the Rauza site was a cache of luster ware cups and bowls (Nos. 101 and 102) which resemble the beautiful vessels from Rayy, but were probably imported from some center like Kashan in eastern Iran. The examples of glazed pottery found at Lashkari Bazaar resemble types found in the region of Bokkhara and Samarkand (No. 110).

These scanty fragments from the brief span of Ghaznavid glory—from the eleventh to the thirteenth century—present a kind of eclectic anthology of the finest forms and techniques of Islamic art drawn from all parts of Iran. This importation of Iranian forms parallels the assimilation of Persian taste in the beginnings of the Mogul empire, with the difference that the civilization established by Mahmud did not survive long enough to develop these borrowings into a national idiom. The Ghaznavid civilization, during its relatively short span of florescence as an embodiment of the finest ex-

pression of Islamic art in Iran, is like a tangible illustration of the words of a Nashī inscription on one of the marble reliefs from Ghazni: "Sufficiency, perfection, beauty, elevation."

Fig. 14. Ghazni, Palace of Ma'sud III. The courtyard, showing marble slabs decorated with inscriptions.

98

The fragments of marble sculpture, bronze, and pottery from these two centers of Islamic civilization in Afghanistan date from the great period of Ghaznavid culture from the eleventh to the early thirteenth centuries.

101

102

103

104

105

109 106 108

107

98. RELIEF OF LION
Marble, carved on both sides; h. 14½ in. (37 cm.)

KM 64.2.1 (from Ghazni)

The heraldic quality of this beast, like other examples of Ghaznavid sculpture in marble, suggests a derivation from Sasanian or even earlier Western Asiatic art forms, which appear to have enjoyed a kind of immortality through the centuries of Islamic civilization. The reverse has a flat decoration of highly conventionalized foliate motifs.

99. HUNTING SCENE (obverse)
EPIGRAPHICAL NASHI (reverse)
Marble; h. 17⅛ in. (43.5 cm.)

KM 64.2.2 (from Ghazni)

A royal hunter attacked by a lion is portrayed on the obverse of this marble slab. Fleeing antelopes appear in the background. This is a motif repeated over and over again in the Sasanian silver plates devoted to scenes of the chivalric hunting exploits of Bahram Gur and Khusrau II. Even the style, realized in flat shapes that seem appliquéd to the background, recalls the technique of Sasanian metalwork. On the reverse appears a conventionalized plant design and, in the plinth, a file of running beasts that remind us of the realistic animals of the Sasanian hunting scenes at Taq-i-Bustan. Above, a Nashi inscription reads: "Sufficiency, perfection, beauty, elevation."

100. VASE WITH STAMPED DECOR
(from Lashkari Bazaar)
Pottery; h. 6¾ in. (17.1 cm.)

LB 1611

Pottery of a similar type, with molded geometric and floral motifs of the ninth and tenth centuries, has been found at Samarra and in Palestine. The direct prototypes for this ware at Lashkari Bazaar are perhaps to be found in Eastern Iranian ceramics of the eleventh and twelfth centuries.

J. 191; AAA 195; MDAFA, XVIII, Pl. VII, 45.

101. BOWL WITH PALACE SCENE
Luster ware; diam. 8½ in. (21.7 cm.)

KM 63.2.1 (from Ghazni)

This large bowl, painted in a sepia-gilt luster with a greenish cast, is an example of a technique of painting in metallic pigments on previously glazed vessels that was developed as early as the ninth century in Egypt and Mesopotamia. From there it was introduced to Rayy and Kashan in the thirteenth century, and one of these famous Iranian kilns is the probable source for the present specimen. The scene filling the center of the bowl represents the entry of a lord and his entourage into a palace gate. The design is possibly a reflection of a lost school of Seljuk miniature painting. In the outer border of the bowl is a decoration composed of meaningless Cufic letters.

J. 192; I. 177, tav. LX; AAA 196, 197.

102. BOWL WITH MEDALLIONS OF
BIRDS AND INSCRIPTIONS
Luster ware; diam. 7⅝ in. (19.4 cm.)

KM 63.2.2 (from Ghazni)

This example of luster ware, decorated with a green-brown glaze on a white ground, resembles the ceramics of Gurgan and Kashan of the early thirteenth century. The ornament of the interior of the vessel comprises circles containing ducks in flight and two zones of inscriptions.

J. 193; I. 178; AAA 198, 199.

103. DISH WITH ZODIACAL SIGNS
Brass; diam. 9⅜ in. (23.6 cm.)

KM 58.2.61 (from Shahr-i-Gholghola)

The decoration of this bowl, possibly the pan of a scale, consists of incised designs including a sphinx in the center or bottom of the dish, ringed by medallions with representations of the signs of the zodiac. These monster forms, in their heraldic quality, have parallels in pottery designs and are reminiscent of pre-Islamic Iranian types.

J. 194; AAA 200.

104. LAMPSTAND

Bronze; h. 27½ in. (70 cm.)

KM 58.2.76   (from Ghazni)

The hemispherical base is supported on three for-malized animal feet. The hexagonal shaft, as well as the vase-like members that enclose it at top and bottom, is decorated with a pierced and incised design of geometric interlaces and palmettes. A decorative Cufic inscription runs around the shoul-der of the base. Lampstands of this type have been found in some numbers at Maimana in Afghan Turkestan. It is possible that bronzes of this type were made in Samarkand or Bokkhara.

I. 162, tav. LXI.

105. INCENSE BURNER

Bronze; h. 5¾ in. (14.6 cm.)

KM 58.2.41   (from Ghazni)

In a strange way this small object resembles a model of an observatory dome, with the pointed cupola divided by raised intersecting ribs. The drum is ornamented with a beautiful foliate Nashī inscrip-tion incised and inlaid with red copper wire. The vault of the vessel is of pierced metal, again deco-rated with copper inlay. The place of manufacture is probably Eastern Iran of the twelfth or thirteenth century.

I. 161, tav. LXIII.

106. EWER

Bronze; h. 8¼ in. (21 cm.)

KM 58.2.17   (from Ghazni)

The body of the polylobed vessel rests on a circular foot and is decorated with two bands of foliated Nashī inscriptions. In the center of each gore is a medallion with an incised conventionalized bird ultimately derived from the heraldic fowl of Sasan-ian textile design. This vessel, like others of the same type, is probably a product of Khorasan of the late twelfth century.

I. 156, tav. LXII.

107. BASE OF LAMPSTAND

Bronze; diam. 8⅝ in. (22 cm.); h. 10⅛ in. (25.7 cm.)

KM 58.2.83   (from Ghazni)

This beautiful base of a lampstand consists of two circular bases, surmounted by a drum pierced by twelve arched openings. Above these elements a low cupola for the support of the stand proper rises just below the circular stem. The most prom-inent features of the decoration of the cupola are the figures of two lions and two bulls in high relief, which might be regarded as a final separation of the antagonists in the famous symplegmas of Achaemenid sculpture at Persepolis. The ground of the hemisphere is beautifully incised with me-dallions containing equestrian hunters and birds. Below the animals which are in relief are cartouches incised with designs of running animals in a foliate spiral pattern. The incised design is complemented, as usual in these vessels, with decorative Cufic in-scriptions. The openings pierced in the drum of the vessel suggest that it may have served as an incense burner in addition to its function of sup-porting the lampstand. This object was possibly made in Ghazni in the twelfth century under strong Iranian and Mesopotamian influences.

I. 164, tav. LXII.

108. EWER

Bronze; h. 12¼ in. (31 cm.)

KM 58.2.186   (from Ghazni)

The decoration consists of bands of Cufic inscrip-tions surrounding a variety of rosette and arabesque designs. The lines of the design are encrusted with inlaid silver. Two lions in relief appear on the neck of the vessel, together with a disk and rosette de-sign. The shape and the technique of this vessel are believed to have originated in Khorasan in the twelfth century.

I. 155.

109. EWER

Bronze; h. 12¼ in. (31 cm.)

KM 58.2.18 (from Ghazni)

Pitchers of this shape and with animal handles in the round derive from Sasanian prototypes, both in glass and metalwork. Their influence is reflected in T'ang pottery and in bronze ewers of the Tempyō period in Japan. Examples from Khorasan have the same shape, and the lion in relief on the neck of the vessel; other similar ewers have been discovered at Maimana and Kandahar. The present example is probably an import from Eastern Iran of the twelfth century.

110. BOWL

Painted and glazed pottery; diam. 10½ in. (26.5 cm.)

KM 63.6.3 (LB 1275) (from Lashkari Bazaar)

This beautiful bowl, painted in black and brown on a cream ground, was probably an import from Gurgan or Kashan in the twelfth or early thirteenth century. (Not illustrated.)

MDAFA, XVIII, Pl. XX, 331.

111. BOWL

Glazed pottery; diam. 6⅞ in. (17.5 cm.)

KM 58.4.324 (from Shahr-i-Gholghola)

The body of the vessel is a yellowish cream, with a geometric design in green in the center and a brown Cufic inscription filling the interior rim. Fragments of this type of ware have been found in great quantities at the citadel in the Bāmiyān Valley which was totally destroyed by Ghengiz Khan in 1222. Although possibly of local manufacture, this pottery is patterned on Eastern Iranian ceramics of the twelfth and thirteenth centuries. (Not illustrated.)

BIBLIOGRAPHY

KEY TO ABBREVIATIONS

KM: Kabul Museum registration number.

AAA: *Ancient Art of Afghanistan (Afuganisutan Kodai Bijutsu)*, Tokyo, 1964.

AJA: *American Journal of Archaeology*.

Annali: Umberto Scerrato, "Oggetti metallici di età islamica in Afghanistan," *Annali dell' Istituto Orientale di Napoli*, N.S. IX, (1960), pp. 95–130.

Encyclopedia: *Encyclopedia of World Art*, New York.

I: *L'Afghanistan dalla Preistoria all'Islam. Mostra dei capolavori del Museo di Kabul*, Turin, 1961.

J: *Exhibition of Ancient Art of Afghanistan (Afuganisutan Kodai Bijutsuten)*, Tokyo, 1963.

MDAFA: *Mémoires de la délégation archéologique française en Afghanistan*.

RA: *Revue Archéologique*.

RIASA: *Rivista dell'Istituto Nazionale d'Archeologia e Storia dell'Arte*.

GENERAL WORKS:

L'Afghanistan dalla preistoria all'Islam, Mostra dei capolavori del Museo di Kabul, Turin, 1961.

Curiel, R., and Schlumberger, D., *Trésors monétaires d'Afghanistan*, MDAFA, (Paris), XIV (1953).

Dagens, B., Le Berre, M., and Schlumberger, D., *Monuments préislamiques d'Afghanistan*, MDAFA, (Paris), XIX (1964).

Deydier, H., *Contribution à l'étude de l'art du Gandhāra*, Paris, 1950.

———, *Exhibition of Ancient Art of Afghanistan*, Tokyo, 1963.

Ghirshman, R., *Les Chionites-Hephthalites*, MDAFA, (Cairo), XIII (1948).

Mizuno, S., Casal, J-M., Rowland, B., Schlumberger, D., and Yoshikawa, I., *Ancient Art of Afghanistan*, Tokyo, 1964.

Wilson, H. H., *Ariana Antiqua . . . with a Memoir on the Buildings called Topes by C. Masson, Esq.*, London, 1841.

MUNDIGAK:

Casal, J-M., *Fouilles de Mundigak*, MDAFA, (Paris), XVII, 2 vols., (1961).

———, "Quatre campagnes de fouilles à Mundigak," *Arts Asiatiques*, 1954, I, 3.

Mode, H., *Das Frühe Indien*, Stuttgart, 1959, pp. 27 ff.

BACTRIA, GENERAL WORKS:

Le Page, M.-Th. Allouche, *L'Art monétaire des royaumes Bactriens. Essai d'interprétation de la symbolique réligieuse grec-orientale du III au I siècle av. J. C.*, Paris, 1956.

Bussagli, M., s.v. "Afghanistan," in *Enciclopedia Universale dell'Arte*, I, Venezia-Roma, 1958.

Foucher, A., and Bazin-Foucher, Mme. E., *La vieille route de l'Inde de Bactres à Taxila*, MDAFA, (Paris), I, 2 vols., (1942–47).

Gardner, P., *Catalogue of Coins in the British Museum: Greek and Scythic Kings of Bactria and India*, London, 1886.

Narain, A. K., *The Indo-Greeks*, Oxford, 1957.

Tarn, W. W., *The Greeks in Bactria and India*, 2ª ed., Cambridge, 1951.

GRAECO-BACTRIAN ART:

Dalton, O. M., *The Treasure of the Oxus*, 3rd ed., London, 1964.

Hallade, M., s.v. "Bactriani centri," in *Enciclopedia Universale dell'Arte*, II, 1958.

Trever, K. B., *Pamiatniki Greko-Baktrijskogo Iskusstva*, Moskva-Leningrad, 1940.

————, s.v. "Bactriana, arte della," in *Enciclopedia dell'Arte Antica Classica ed Orientale*, II, Roma, 1959.

BACTRIA UNDER THE KUSHANS:

Dagens, B., *Sculptures de Bactriane*, MDAFA, (Paris), XIX (1964).

Hackin, J., *Fouilles de Kunduz*, MDAFA, (Paris), VIII (1959).

Schlumberger, D., "Descendants non-méditerranéens de l'art grec," *Syria*, XXXVII, 1960, p. 142 sgg.

————, "Le temple de Surkh Kotal en Afghanistan," *Journal Asiatique*, 1952, 433; 1954, 161; 1955, 209.

BEGRĀM, GENERAL WORKS:

Ghirshman, R., *Begrām, Recherches archéologiques et historiques sur les Koushans*, MDAFA, (Cairo), XII (1946).

Hackin, J., Hackin, J. R., *Recherches archéologiques à Begrām (chantier n. 2, 1937)*, MDAFA, (Paris), IX, 2 vols., (1939).

Hackin, J., *Nouvelles recherches archéologiques à Begrām (1939-1940)*, with the collaboration of J. R. Hackin, J. Carl, P. Hamelin; comparative studies by J. Auboyer, V. Elisséeff, O. Kurz, Ph. Stern, MDAFA, (Paris), XI, 2 vols., (1954).

BEGRĀM, GRAECO-ROMAN FINDS:

Coarelli, F., *I vetri dipinti di Begrām e l'Illiade ambrosiana*, Roma, 1961.

Picard, Ch., "Oscilla de plâtre alexandrins au trésor de Begrām," RA, 1960, I, pp. 120 ff.

Richter, G. M. A., "Ancient Plaster Casts of Greek Metalware," AJA, 42, 1958, pp. 369 ff.

Wheeler, M., *Rome beyond the Imperial Frontiers*, London, 1954.

BEGRĀM, IVORIES:

Ghosh, A., "Taxila," *Ancient India*, 4, 1944-45, Pl. XX.

Hallade, M., s.v. "Avorio e osso," in *Enciclopedia Universale dell'Arte*, II, 1958, pp. 276 ff.

Maiuri, A., "Statuetta eburnea di arte indiana a Pompeii," *Le Arti*, I, 1939, p. 111 ff.

HADDA:

Bachhofer, L., "Zur Plastik von Hadda," *Ostasiatische Zeitschrift*, VII, 1931, 106-111.

Barthoux, J., *Les fouilles de Hadda, Figures et figurines*, MDAFA, (Paris), VI (1930).

————, *Les fouilles de Hadda, Stūpas et sites*, MDAFA, (Paris), IV (1933).

Dagens, B., *Fragments de sculpture inédits*, MDAFA, (Paris), XIX (1964).

Hackin, J., "Sculptures gréco-bouddhiques du Kapiśa," *Monuments et Mémoires* (Fondation Piot), XXVIII, 1, Paris, 1925–26.

Rowland, B., "The Hellenistic Tradition in Northwestern India," *The Art Bulletin*, March 1949, XXXI, 1.

SHOTORAK AND PĀITĀVĀ, GANDHĀRA SCULPTURE:

Bussagli, M., *L'Arte del Gandhāra in Pakistan e i suoi incontri con l'arte dell'Asia Centrale*, (Catalogue of Exhibition: *Arte dell Gandhāra e dell'Asia Centrale*), Roma, 1958.

———, "Osservazioni sulla persistenza delle forme ellenistiche nell'arte del Gandhāra," RIASA, N.S. V–VI, 1956–1957 (publ. 1958), pp. 149 ff.

Deydier, H., *Contribution à l'étude de l'art du Gandhāra*, Paris, 1950.

Meunié, J., *Shotorak*, MDAFA, (Paris), X (1942).

Rowland, B., "Gandhāra, Rome and Mathurā. The Early Relief Style," *Archives of the Chinese Art Society of America*, X, 1956, pp. 8 ff.

———, "Rome and Gandhāra," *East and West*, IX, 1958, pp. 199 ff.

BĀMIYĀN AND KAKRAK:

Godard, A. and Y., and Hackin, J. *Les antiquités bouddhiques de Bāmiyān*, MDAFA, (Paris), II (1928).

Hackin, J., *Archéologie bouddhique (L'oeuvre de la délégation archéologique française en Afghanistan—1922-32)*, Tokyo, 1933.

Hackin, J., and J. R., *Le site archéologique de Bāmiyān. Guide du visiteur*, Paris, 1934.

Hackin, J. and Carl, J., *Nouvelles recherches archéologiques à Bāmiyān*, MDAFA, (Paris), III (1933).

Rowland, B., *The Wall-Paintings of India, Central Asia, and Ceylon*, Boston, 1938.

———, "The Dating of the Sasanian Paintings at Bāmiyān and Dukhtar-i-Nushirvan," *Bulletin of the Iranian Institute*, VI–VII, 1946.

KOTAL KHAIR KHANEH:

Hackin, J., and Carl, J., *Recherches archéologiques au col de Khair Khaneh*, MDAFA, (Paris), VII (1936).

FONDUKISTAN:

Barrett, D., "Sculptures of the Shāhi Period," *Oriental Art*, 1957, III, 2.

Hackin, J., "Le monastère bouddhique de Fondukistan," in *Diverses recherches archéologiques en Afghanistan*, MDAFA, (Paris), VIII (1959) (published in English in *Journal of the Greater India Society*, vol. VII, 1940).

Rowland, B., *The Art and Architecture of India*, Harmondsworth and Baltimore, 1953 and 1966.

———, "The Bejewelled Buddha in Afghanistan," *Artibus Asiae*, XXIV, 1, 1961.

ISLAMIC PERIOD, GENERAL WORKS AND GHAZNAVID ART:

Bombaci, A., s.v. "Ghaznavidi," *Enciclopedia Universale dell'Arte*, VI, 1961 (also in English Edition *Encyclopaedia of World Art*).

———, "Introduction to the Excavations at Ghazni," *East and West*, 10, 1959, pp. 3 ff.

Bussagli, M., s.v. "Afghanistan," *Enciclopedia Universale dell'Arte*, I, 1958 (also in English Edition *Encyclopaedia of World Art*).

Gardin, J-C., *Lashkari Bazaar, une résidence royale ghaznévide: céramiques et monnaies*, MDAFA, (Paris), XVIII (1963).

Scerrato, U., "The first two Excavations Campaigns at Ghazni, 1957–58, (Summary Report)," *East and West*, 1959, pp. 23 ff.

————, "Oggetti metallici di età islamica in Afghanistan, I. Antiquario di Kandahar," *Annali dell'Istituto Orientale di Napoli*, n.s. IX, 1960, pp. 95 ff.

Schlumberger, D., "Les Palais Ghaznavides de Lashkari Bazaar," *Syria*, 1952, pp. 252 ff.

KABUL AND RELATED SITES:

Carl, J., *Le monastère bouddhique de Tépé Marandjān*, MDAFA, (Paris), VIII (1959).

Hackin, J., and Carl, J., *Recherches archéologiques au col de Khair Khaneh*, MDAFA, (Paris), VII (1936).

Schlumberger, D., "Le marbre Scorretti," *Journal Asiatique*, 1955.

CREDITS

The map of Afghanistan on p. 12 is reproduced by permission of *The Encyclopedia of World Art*, Copyright 1959, McGraw-Hill Publishing Co., Ltd.

The photograph on p. 11 is by Marc Riboud, Magnum Photos.

The following photographs are by Josephine Powell, Rome; 12, 51, 53, 87, 97, 98, 99, 102, 108, 109.

The following photographs were provided by the Museo Civico di Torino, through the courtesy of the Director, Dr. Vittorio Viale; 7, 8, 13, 18, 19, 21 (color), 24, 26, 28 (black-and-white), 35, 43, 44, 50, 56, 62, 63, 64, 67, 77 (color), 93 (color), 94, 104, 105, 106, 107.

The following photographs were provided by the Nihon Keizai Shimbun, Tokyo, through the courtesy of Mr. Jiro Enjoji; 1, 2, 3, 4, 5, 9, 11, 14, 15, 17, 20, 22, 25, 27, 28 (color), 29, 30, 31 (color), 32, 33, 34, 36, 37, 38, 39, 40, 45, 47, 48, 49, 52, 54, 57, 58, 59, 60, 68, 70, 71, 72, 73, 75 (color), 76, 78, 79, 80, 81, 82, 84, 85, 86, 88, 90, 91, 92, 95, 96, 100, 101, 103. The two color photographs are by the Sakimoto Photo Research Lab, Tokyo.

Photograph Number 61 is reproduced from Barthoux, *Les Fouilles de Hadda*, *Figures et Figurines*, MDAFA VI, Pl. 36, by permission of the Musée Guimet, Paris.

Text figures:

Figs. 1, 7, 8, 13; Benjamin Rowland, Jr.

Figs. 10, 11A, 11B, 12; John Rosenfield.

Fig. 2 is reproduced from Maffei, *Gemme antiche figurate*, No. 29.

Fig. 3; Museo Nazionale, Naples.

Fig. 4; Dominique Darbois.

Fig. 5; The Fogg Art Museum, Harvard University, Cambridge, Massachusetts.

Fig. 6; Alinari, Florence.

Fig. 9A; Museum for Central Asian Antiquities, New Delhi.

Fig. 9B; Photo Vahé, Teheran.

Fig. 14; IsMEO (Istituto Italiano per il Medio ed Estremo Oriente), Rome.

Catalogue designed by Virginia Field, Assistant Director, Asia House Gallery
Color engravings by Brüder Hartmann, Berlin
Black-and-white engravings by Powers and Conway
Printed and bound by Clarke & Way, Inc., New York